"Transcendental Meditation seems to be taking a firm hold on the American mind."

—Anatole Broyard
New York Times, March 1975

"1975's biggest cultural whirlwind."

New York Times, August 1975

"I started the Transcendental Meditation program because I felt like I wasn't doing anything for myself, for the growth of my system. I was wasting time. I wasn't reading, I wasn't doing anything, I wasn't really growing. So I started meditating because of the effects it has on your body and your mind, and it's done a great deal for me. It's made me feel like I am helping myself, and through that I can get along with other people and maybe help them a little more with different situations or problems. The main thing though, I feel like it's helping me, and that in itself has done so much for my whole togetherness. I feel like I'm not wasting myself, that I am helping my mind and my body live life in the right way. And I've enjoyed it and I'm going to keep on enjoying it.

Joe Namath
Quarterback, New York Jets

"My blood pressure went down ten points. My wife said my disposition improved, and minor stresses and strains of life around Washington didn't bother me any more."

Major General Franklin M. Davis
Commandant, U.S. Army War College

Will this book teach me how to do TM?

This book will tell you what the Transcendental Meditation program is, and why you might like to enjoy the TM technique. But you must learn the TM technique personally from a trained teacher, who will guide you on the basis of your own experiences as you learn the technique.

There are over 6,000 teachers of the Transcendental Meditation program in the U.S. alone with TM centers in nearly every city.

Why do you keep referring to the TM technique and the TM program? I thought it was all just TM.

The TM *technique* is a specific, scientific practice. The TM *program* includes twice-daily practice of the TM technique and other educational services, which we will talk about in chapter 4. "Transcendental Meditation" and "TM" identify the specific educational programs offered only by the various nonprofit organizations authorized by Maharishi Mahesh Yogi.

Therefore, participating in programs identified by these terms assures you of receiving the technique, programs, and benefits that are described in this book and verified by scientific research conducted around the world.

How to Enjoy the Rest of Your Life

Denise Denniston and Peter McWilliams
Illustrated by Barry Geller

VERSEMONGER PRESS

The TM Book: How to Enjoy the Rest of Your Life

A Price/Stern/Sloan—Versemonger Book

ISBN 0-8431-0520-8
Library of Congress catalogue number 75-13848

Publisher
Versemonger Press
5806 Elizabeth
Allen Park, Michigan 48101

Product Development
Cobb/Dunlop Publisher Services, Inc.

Distributed by
Price / Stern / Sloan Publishers, Inc.
410 N. LaCienega Blvd
Los Angeles CA 90048

and by
MIU Press, Box 370, Livingston Manor NY

For individual copies, please
write to Versemonger Press,
(address above).

Published simultaneously in Canada by Price / Stern / Sloan-Versemonger

Distributed in Canada by Gage Publishing
164 Commander Blvd
P.O. Box 5000
Agincourt, Ontario

TABLE OF CONTENTS

We are delighted to thank all those who helped in the preparation of this book — particularly: Allen Cobb, Bob Cobb, David Dunlop, Stan Crowe, Myron Feld, Nan Geller, Mary Jo Kaiser, Peter Muldavin and Mike Smith.

Our own Transcendental Meditation teachers: Terry Gustafson, Al Bruns, and Bob Markowitz,

and Jerry Jarvis, for all his help, and especially for coming up with eight-elevenths of the title.

The authors of *The TM Book* are teachers of the Transcendental Meditation program. They have been personally trained and qualified by Maharishi Mahesh Yogi.

Denise Denniston became a teacher in 1971. Since then she has taught TM in Omaha, Nebraska, Los Angeles, California and New York City. She has worked at the United States National Center and at the International Center of the World Plan Executive Council. This is her first book.

Peter McWilliams is the author of eleven books of poetry. He became a teacher of the TM program in 1972 and has since taught in Detroit, Michigan and Los Angeles, California.

Barry Geller, who illustrated this book, is head of the design department of Maharishi International University Press, the international production facility for the TM movement in Europe.

This book is dedicated
with profound love
and deepest gratitude to
MAHARISHI MAHESH YOGI
Founder of the
Science of Creative Intelligence
and chief proponent of its practical aspect,
the Transcendental Meditation program

Photo by Victor Raymond

I keep hearing about the Transcendental Meditation program. Why is it becoming so popular?

The Transcendental Meditation (or TM) technique was introduced to the United States by Maharishi Mahesh Yogi in 1959. People started the TM technique, liked it, and told their friends, who started and in turn told *their* friends, who then also started. Students especially appreciated the value of Maharishi's message: "Man is born to enjoy, to create, and to radiate happiness." By the end of the 1960's, hundreds of thousands of people were practicing the TM technique. The reason most of these people began is because their friends had recommended it.

Then, in 1970, Dr. Robert Keith Wallace of the U.S. began scientific research into the effects of the Transcendental Meditation technique on the mind and body. In his first set of experiments he discovered that during the TM technique, the metabolic rate is reduced by 16% in a matter of minutes. During sleep the metabolic rate is usually reduced by only 12% over a period of many hours. This means that the TM technique quickly provides a state of rest that is much deeper than sleep. These findings were made even more remarkable by the fact that the mind remains alert and awake during this rest—that there is no loss of consciousness as there is during sleep. Dr. Wallace called this unique state of mind and body functioning "restful alertness."

Scientists the world over began studying the effects of the TM technique. The results of these studies, printed in dozens of scientific journals and reported in hundreds of newspapers and magazines, have been responsible for the increasing interest in the TM program over the past few years. These scientific studies offer a vision of man with greater clarity of mind, improved health, and freedom from tension, anxiety, stress. The Transcendental Meditation program changes the quality of life from poverty, emptiness, and suffering to abundance, fulfillment, and happiness.

Excuse my skepticism, but that sounds hopelessly idealistic.

Only a few years ago diseases such as polio and smallpox (not to mention cholera, diphtheria, typhus, typhoid, and whooping cough) were accepted as part of the human condition. Those who thought otherwise were considered hopelessly idealistic. Then came the discovery of vaccines. Today, wherever the vaccines are used, these diseases are no longer found.

The TM technique is practical. Science has proven that it provides deep rest, removes tension and fatigue, and increases mental clarity and intelligence. (More of the scientific results later.) The TM technique is a great scientific discovery. It makes suffering in life a thing of the past. By the end of the book we hope you'll agree that it's not that idealistic after all.

I've heard how difficult meditation is, with concentration and exercises, and I know I could never make my mind a blank.

Neither could we. There are many misconceptions about the words "transcendental" and "meditation." People have the idea that "transcendental" has something to do with Thoreau and Emerson and Walden Pond, and most people are *sure* that "meditation" involves severe concentration, brown rice diets, pretzel postures—and wasn't there that swami on "You Asked For It!" who sat on nails and ate glass? It would help our understanding to discuss the many things that the TM program is *not*.

Alright. What is not the Transcendental Meditation program?

Excellent question!

Chapter 1

What the TM Program Is Not

the TM program does NOT involve religious beliefs

The TM program is not a religion? I've heard it was just some Westernized form of Hinduism.

No, no—it's absurd to assume that just because the TM technique comes from India it must be some Hindu practice. Italy is considered a Catholic country. Galileo, an Italian, discovered that the earth is round. The fact that the earth is round is no more connected with the Catholic Church than the TM technique is connected with the Hindu religion. The TM technique is a scientific discovery which happens to come from India. As with all scientific discoveries, it works everywhere because it involves the basic laws of nature. The TM program does not involve any religious belief or practice — Hindu or otherwise. Just like bathing always works to get you clean, the TM program is a universally applicable practice for getting the most out of life.

Isn't Maharishi a monk?

Yes, he is. Many great scientists and thinkers are men of profound religious convictions. Gregor Mendel, who discovered the laws of genetics, was himself a Jesuit priest. Einstein often spoke of his "cosmic religious sense." A scientist's personal religious beliefs have no bearing on the validity of his contributions to science.

Does TM conflict with any form of religion?

No. People of any religion practice the TM technique. In fact, they find the increased clarity of mind brought about through the TM program greatly broadens the comprehension and enhances the appreciation of their individual religious practices. Priests practice it, rabbis practice it, ministers practice it, and they recommend the TM program to their congregations.

Rabbi Raphael Levine
Rabbi Emeritus of Temple De Hirsh Sinai
Seattle, Washington

"The TM program is not a religion. It has nothing to do with religion except as the easiest technique I have yet discovered for making religion become more alive, more meaningful, by helping people to live the way their religion teaches them to live — on the level of love and self-giving.

"What impresses me about the TM technique is its simplicity. Instead of concentration, contemplation or strenous self-disciplining exercises to subdue the self-centeredness which we have always believed is our human nature, the TM technique is effortless and enjoyable, practiced twenty minutes twice a day, achieving this miracle for us not by the disciplines of self-denial, but by the joy and happiness of self-enlargement, the enlargement of our state of consciousness; and the miracle is that it works!"

Rev. Leo McAllister
Catholic priest
Pastor of the Immaculate Conception Church, Sacramento, California
For the past six years Chaplain to the Assembly,
California State Legislature

"I am writing this letter to allay any fears, anxieties, or misconceptions which Catholics may have concerning the practice of the Transcendental Meditation program. I have been using the Transcendental Meditation technique for the past seven months.

"It is not a religion or a religious practice. It in no way conflicts with a person's belief in God or in his church. It is a simple natural technique whereby, through regular practice, one can rid oneself of stresses of the mind and enjoy deep rest and relaxation.

"There are many benefits which result from regular practice. A person's relationship to God and the practice of one's faith should be enhanced rather than diminished, by the use of the Transcendental Meditation program. One becomes much more sensitive to the presence of God in our universe and the interdependence and harmony which He intended to exist between peoples and things.

"I am happy to say that I can recommend it highly."

Rev. Karl E. Lutze
Ordained Lutheran clergyman
Theology Professor at Valparaiso University

"I am pleased to hear of your interest in the Transcendental Meditation program — primarily because I not only have read about it, but I have looked into it to explore its usefulness for me and now participate in the program with regularity.

"I, as you, had some initial reservations about the TM technique from a religious and theological standpoint. It was not without careful and serious study and reflection that I attempted to learn whether or not this art stemming as it does from the traditions of the Far East might be compatible or in fact in conflict with my Christian faith.

"I find it to be particularly consonant with my Christian life to care for myself—my body, my mind, all of me—in such a way as to be at my best for my Lord and His service. We sometimes in churchly parlance call this 'good stewardship of self.' That I find this discipline of meditation affording me a relief from stress, a kind of creative rest for the mind and an ordering of thought and plans suggests that I'm far more ready for better performance of my tasks than I would otherwise be.

"I do not find the Transcendental Meditation program an alternative to Christian faith; I practice it within the context of my Christian life. Nor does my calling upon the exercise of the TM technique imply that my Christian faith or religion is inadequate, any more than my efforts to get enough sleep, proper diet, exercise, and recreation would imply an inadequacy in my religion.

"I regard meditation as another of God's good gifts to me like friendships and education and any number of other good things that enrich my life and equip me for living it well. As with all gifts, I do not let the gift mean more to me than the Giver.

"I shall be glad to converse with you further on your and my experience with the TM program should you wish to do so."

What about atheists?

Atheists enjoy the Transcendental Meditation program for the same reason the devoutly religious enjoy it—it involves no dogma, belief, or philosophy. The technique is purely scientific and produces scientifically verifiable results.

But doesn't meditation have something to do with knowing God? Doesn't that make the TM program essentially a religious practice?

The TM program has something to do with knowing *anything*. It makes the mind more orderly, gives the body deep rest, and improves the coordination between the two. This means that with clear awareness we can focus sharply and succeed in activity — whatever our activity may be.

no special diet

Aren't most who practice the TM program vegetarians?

Some are. Many aren't. But then, a lot of nonTMer's are vegetarians, too. The point is, there are no dietary restrictions or recommendations involved with the TM program.

No daily ration of brown rice?

Nope

I can still eat Big Macs?

You can eat anything you want.

This is sounding better and better.

no special clothing

No funny clothes?

No.

How about sandals? Some TM people wear sandals.

And some wear sneakers, or Hush Puppies, or Guccis. We get all kinds. People who enjoy the TM program grow to express their own unique individuality, and this is reflected in their life style, self-expression, and, of course, their clothing.

no exercises

Oh yes! These are yoga postures, aren't they? What do they have to do with the TM technique?

Nothing. These are hatha yoga postures. The word "hatha" means "force"; "yoga" means "union." Postures are physical and require effort. Hatha yoga can be enjoyable, but deep rest and normalizing of the whole nervous system come most quickly and easily through the Transcendental Meditation technique. The technique is an effortless, natural, mental practice that accomplishes the goal of "yoga" (complete integration of the mind, body, and activity) in the most comfortable, effortless way.

Don't the postures accomplish integration?

Exercises certainly can help improve one's health. But since every aspect of physical health depends on the mind and the nervous system, for complete and natural integration of life we need the TM technique. The key factor recommending the TM program is that it gets to the basis of all our mental and physical functioning. There are many ways of traveling from New York to Los Angeles: walking, bicycling, driving—the TM program is like taking a jet, first class: it's the fastest and most comfortable.

the TM technique is not contemplation

What is contemplation?

Contemplation is thinking *about* something (a problem, a philosophical idea) or just letting the mind wander from one idea to the next with no particular direction.

Isn't that what people mean by "meditation"?

Many do, yes. They say "I am meditating" on this or that thought. Some call quiet reflection "meditation," while others glorify their day-dreams with the title "meditation."

The Transcendental Meditation technique is a very specific practice, very different from any of these sorts of "meditation."

no concentration

How is concentration different from contemplation?

Concentration is the rigid fixing of the mind on one particular point, and holding the attention on this point for as long as possible.

My friend had me stare into a candle for the better part of an hour one night.

Yes, a candle is a common concentration point.

It gave me a headache.

Yes, that is a common result.

And the TM technique involves no concentration?

Absolutely *not*!

In the TM technique, isn't one asked to focus on a mantra?

No. A mantra is given during personal instruction (more of this on pages 177 and 182) but one is not asked to *focus* upon it. To control the use of the mantra in any way (saying it once each time one exhales, for example) is a form of concentration, and concentration is *not* part of the TM technique.

the TM technique is not bio-feedback or alpha-wave control

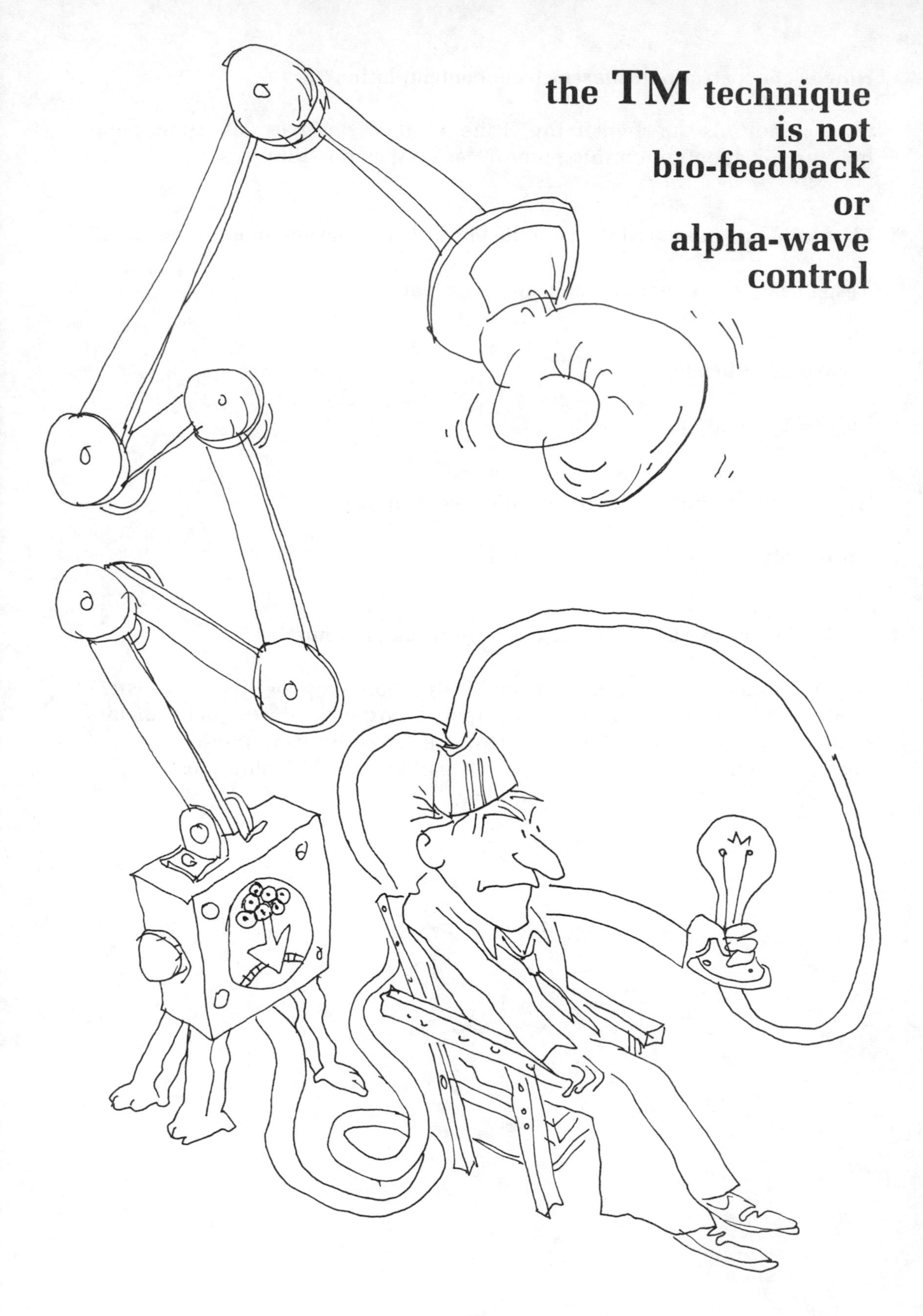

Is the TM technique the same as bio-feedback?

No. Bio-feedback is a process whereby a person learns to control some aspect of the body's functioning which is usually not under conscious control — for example, the heart rate, circulation, or brain activity. This is done by connecting some light or sound with what is being controlled so that the subject can see or hear what his body is doing, and learn to change the light or tone by changing the physiology.

There are two major differences between the TM technique and bio-feedback. First, the TM technique is completely effortless. Everything that happens, happens spontaneously, unlike bio-feedback, which requires conscious control and effort to produce some specific change. The changes in the body and mind during the TM technique come without our willing them or learning to do them.

Second, and even more important, the TM technique produces far more than one specific change such as more alpha waves. It produces a spontaneous state of deep rest and alertness for the body and the mind. This shows up as an integrated physiological response that includes a whole *pattern* of brainwave activity. The brain waves found during the TM technique (including alpha) reflect the unique restful alertness that improves the functioning of every aspect of the mind, the body, and the emotions. It produces these changes simultaneously, in a completely balanced way.

Alpha waves?

Alpha waves are a specific frequency of brain waves, or the electrical activity of the brain, measured on the electroencephalograph (EEG) machine. Since some research several years ago connected alpha waves with meditation, tranquility and subjective good feelings, bio-feedback has been used to train people to produce more alpha activity. Although restfulness does produce alpha, alpha doesn't necessarily produce much restfulness. It doesn't work both ways.

no change of life style

No change of life style?

There is no need to change in any way to start the TM program. There are no pleasures you must abandon, nor any new traditions you must uphold.

So my life would go on without change.

Without *forced* change. Life is always changing. The TM program produces remarkably rapid growth. Your life will continue to change naturally, in the direction of more strength, more effectiveness, and more enjoyment. But remember, you're in full control of your own growth—it's your responsibility every step of the way.

There is no need to change anything to start the TM program?

Right.

chapter 2

What the TM Technique Is

Now that I know what the TM program is not, tell me what the TM technique is.

Let's give you a complete definition first; then we can analyze it point by point.

The Transcendental Meditation technique is a simple, natural, effortless process that allows the mind to experience subtler and subtler levels of the thinking process until thinking is transcended and the mind comes into direct contact with the source of thought.

But please remember that the TM technique produces an experience, and like any experience it is hard to describe or define. No matter how clearly or cleverly we might describe a strawberry, for instance, you would still have only an abstract idea of the strawberry. But when you see a strawberry, feel a strawberry, and taste a strawberry, then the experience becomes very real.

DICTIONARY
DICTIONARY

The source of thought. What's that?

Have you ever had the feeling that thoughts don't just spring to the mind fully formed?

I've never thought about it.

Consider it for a moment. Do thoughts simply pop into the mind, fully formed, or do they seem to come from somewhere deep within the mind, existing at some abstract, more subtle level before they become totally clear?

Well, they're not just there. I guess they do seem to come from someplace.

They seem to come from somewhere within us.

All these thoughts come from one source: a field of pure energy deep within the mind.

You're getting a bit abstract, aren't you?

Let us be abstract just a minute longer, because what we want to find out is what the source of thought is really like.

Every thought has some meaning, some direction. Even a nonsensical thought or a thought in a dream makes some kind of sense to us—we recognize it as a picture, as words, as an emotion, or as an idea. This means that every thought has some kind of intelligent purpose or direction. We don't think at random because thoughts themselves contain intelligence.

So now we know one thing about the source of thought—it has to be creative, a reservoir of intelligence. Every bit of intelligence that we display in our daily lives reflects the intelligence contained in our thoughts.

Also, we experience thousands of thoughts every day—they just keep coming and coming. So they must be coming from a virtually unlimited source of energy.

The source of thought, then, is the source of millions of individual bundles of creativity, intelligence, and energy.

Some people don't seem to display as much intelligence as they might.

Right. We all display different degrees of intelligence in different kinds of activity. That's why we're talking about the TM program—all of us want to display *maximum* intelligence in *everything* we do. Thinking is the basis of action, action is the basis of achievement, and achievement makes us feel fulfilled.

This still seems abstract . . .

Consider it from the scientific point of view. According to physics, everything that exists is built up of layers of energy, one inside another. Einstein demonstrated that matter is just another form of energy with his equation "$E = mc^2$." Also, we notice that in all creation, from the growth of the plants to the movement of the planets, there is great order, or intelligence. Since thoughts also exist, they must be made of the most basic form of energy as well. And they have their source, or basis, in the same field of creative intelligence and energy that underlies all creation.

What does this have to do with the TM technique?

The regular practice of the Transcendental Meditation technique taps this field of energy within ourselves, bringing it out to fully enhance our lives. We tap the source of intelligence, and daily we are more intelligent. We tap the source of energy, and daily we are more energetic. We tap the source of creativity, and daily we are more creative. So the TM technique is a process by which one contacts this source of pure creativity and intelligence at the basis of the thinking process, allowing this creative intelligence to be expressed in greater clarity of mind, greater efficiency of action, and increasingly fulfilling achievements in daily life.

NATURAL
the TM program
is natural

It sounds very complicated.

It *sounds* complicated, but *doing* it isn't. That's because it's perfectly natural. The mind finds contact with this field of pure creative intelligence highly enjoyable. We are naturally drawn toward that which makes us happiest. Friends, loved ones, music—the mind automatically chooses that which gives the most pleasure. To be drawn toward what we enjoy is very natural.

If it's so natural, why do I have to learn it?

Speaking is natural, yet we had to learn how to speak. There is a certain technique to speaking, but once we learn the technique it all seems quite natural. And it *is* quite natural.

To directly contact the source of our own creativity and intelligence is the most natural thing we can do. All we need is the technique.

the TM technique is easy

the **TM** technique is effortless

"Easy" and "effortless"?

Anything that is natural *must* be easy and effortless. It is easy to talk, to eat, to sleep, to enjoy our friends—and because it is so easy it's also effortless. The same is true of the TM technique. Once the technique is learned, the process flows—easily and effortlessly.

Ah! There's the catch! "Once the technique is learned." Just how many years does it take to learn this technique?

Years? Days. Hours, actually. Four two-hour sessions with a qualified teacher of the TM program, and that's it.

And then I do the TM technique whenever I want?

No. The TM technique is practiced twice a day, morning and evening, for 15–20 minutes each time. It's preparation for activity. We sit comfortably anywhere we happen to be: propped up in bed, on a train, in the office, in your living room, anywhere.

This twice—daily practice of the TM technique forms the basis of the TM program.

effective

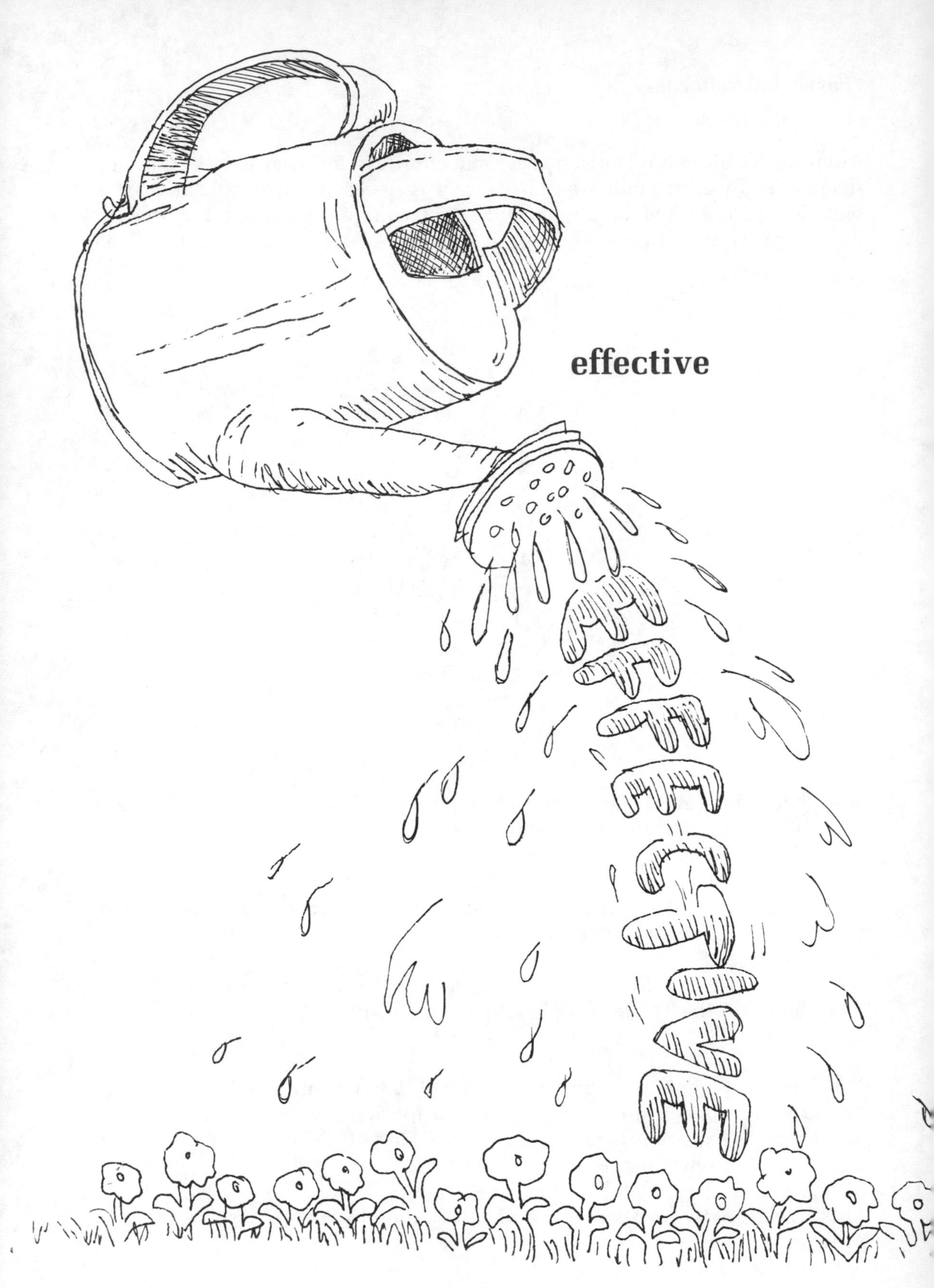

The TM program?

The Transcendental Meditation program fits into your life something like this:

You wake in the morning wishing that sleep had worked a little better. You begin your morning session of the TM technique and contact the source of creative intelligence. Fifteen—twenty minutes later you feel refreshed, awake, alive. As the day wears on and this feeling of freshness wears off, you begin to feel less efficient, more tired. Time for the early-evening period of the TM technique. The deep rest dissolves any stress accumulated during the day and the contact with creative intelligence enlivens the mind so that you are ready to engage in a full evening of enjoyable activities.

the TM program is fun

You've brought out a new concept here: one of deep rest during the Transcendental Meditation technique.

Rest is the basis of all our activity. How well we perform depends on how rested we are. When we have a good night's sleep, the activity of the day is effective and almost effortless. When we have a poor night's sleep, activity is ineffective and very difficult. When we have no rest at all, activity is all but impossible.

So we see that rest is the basis of successful activity. Successful activity leads to fulfillment, and the automatic result of fulfillment is happiness. Thus, basically, our happiness depends upon the quality of our rest. The TM technique provides the deepest state of rest yet measured, deeper even than sleep.

Our days are structured in cycles with a period of rest (night's sleep) and a period of activity (the day and evening). The TM program adds two additional periods of revitalizing rest—making the entire structure of activity more flexible and enjoyable.

Levels of Rest: Change in Metabolic Rate

Change in Metabolic Rate

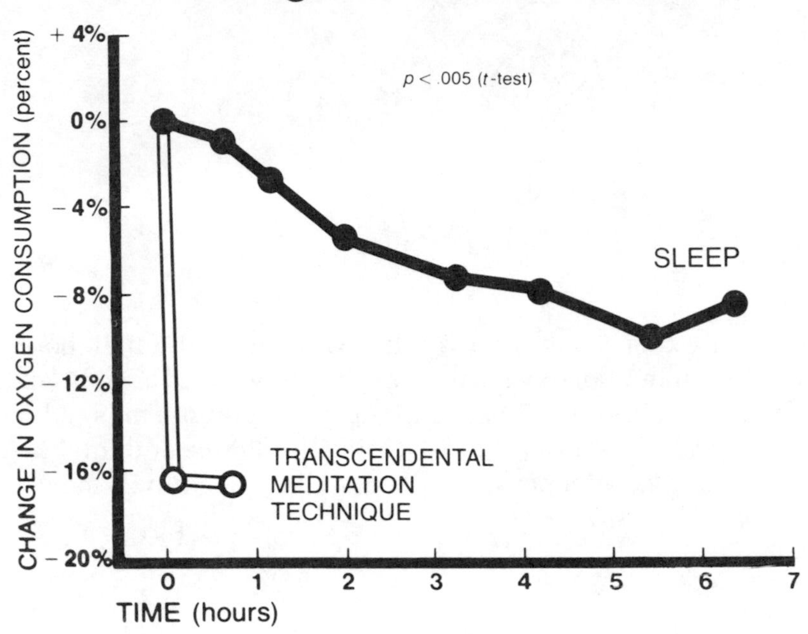

Levels of Rest

Finding: Metabolic rate was obtained by measuring oxygen consumption in 20 subjects during the Transcendental Meditation technique. The study showed that during the TM technique oxygen consumption markedly decreases. The average decrease was 16 percent within the first ten minutes of a session of the Transcendental Meditation technique. Further, the study showed that the partial pressures of oxygen and carbon dioxide in the blood remained essentially constant. The decrease in metabolic rate during the Transcendental Meditation technique was deeper and much quicker than during deep sleep.

Interpretation: The decrease in total oxygen consumption during the Transcendental Meditation technique indicates a unique state of deep rest. This decrease is not caused by manipulation in breathing pattern or forced deprivation of oxygen, but is a natural physiological change due to a lowered requirement for oxygen by the cells during this effortless process.

First Reference: Robert Keith Wallace, "The Physiological Effects of Transcendental Meditation: A Proposed Fourth Major State of Consciousness" (Ph.D. Thesis, Department of Physiology, University of California, Los Angeles, California, U.S.A., 1970).

Second Reference: Robert Keith Wallace, Herbert Benson, and Archie F. Wilson, "A Wakeful Hypometabolic Physiologic State," *American Journal of Physiology* 221, no. 3 (U.S.A.: 1971): 795-799.

Third Reference: Robert Keith Wallace and Herbert Benson, "The Physiology of Meditation," *Scientific American* 226, no. 2 (U.S.A.: 1972): 84–90.

As we can see by this graph, after six hours of sleep the metabolic rate (as measured by the amount of oxygen used by the body) is reduced by about 12%. After only five minutes of the TM technique, the metabolism is reduced more than 16%. This indicates a state of rest during the Transcendental Meditation technique that is much deeper than sleep, and comes much more quickly.

Deeper than sleep? But I thought you said the mind comes into direct contact with the source of *energy*.

It does, which means that everything functions more efficiently, and the body consumes less energy. The TM technique produces a unique state of restful alertness—the body is very deeply rested while the mind is awake and alert.

The mind is more alert during rest? And yet the body is resting deeper than during sleep?

Right. This is a fourth state of consciousness, different from the three we already experience: deep sleep, dreaming, and waking. It is because the body is rested and the mind is still alert that we call this fourth major state of consciousness "restful alertness."

And every time someone does the TM technique they reach this state of restful alertness?

Automatically.

deep sleep consciousness

dreaming consciousness

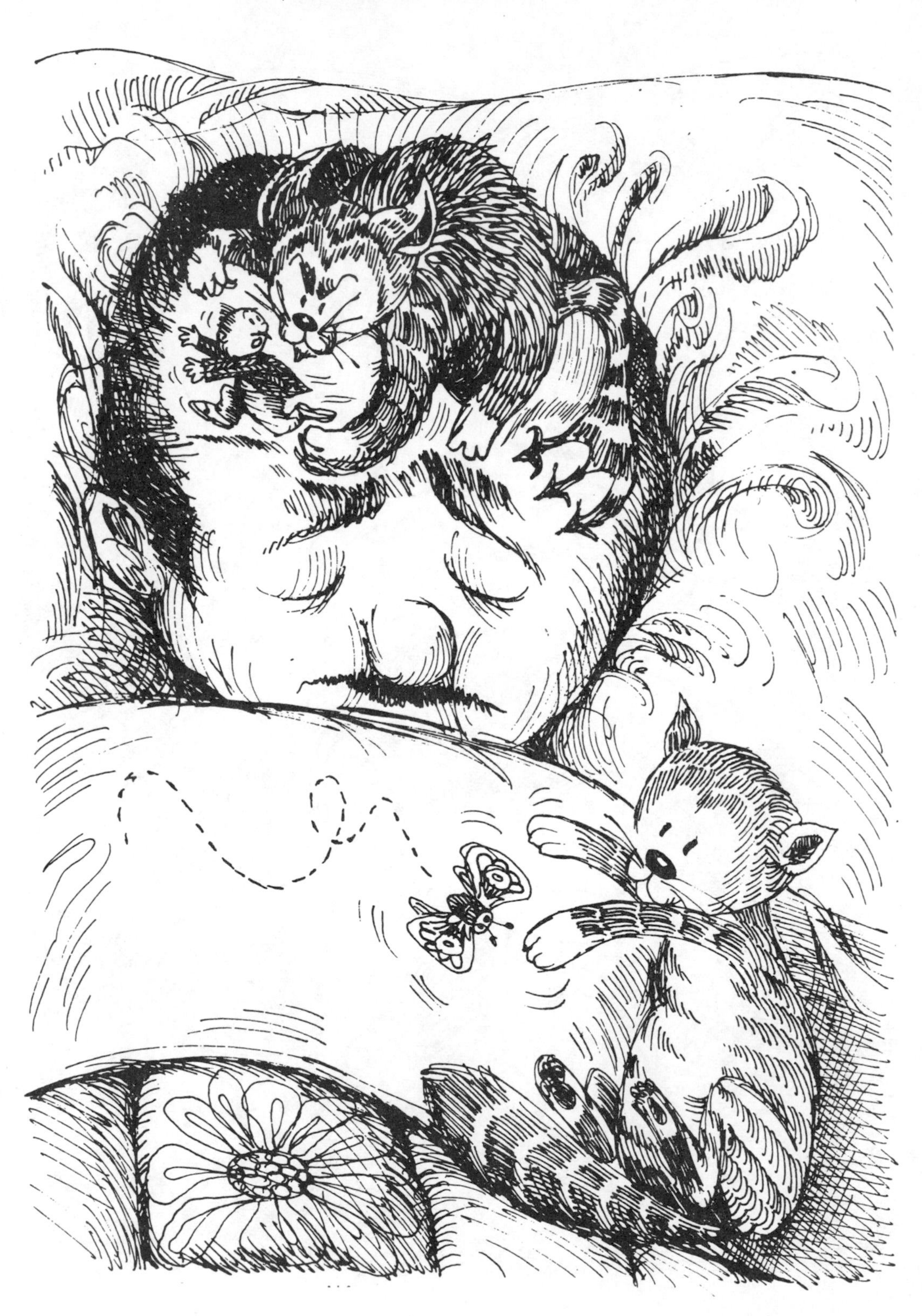

waking consciousness

restful alertness

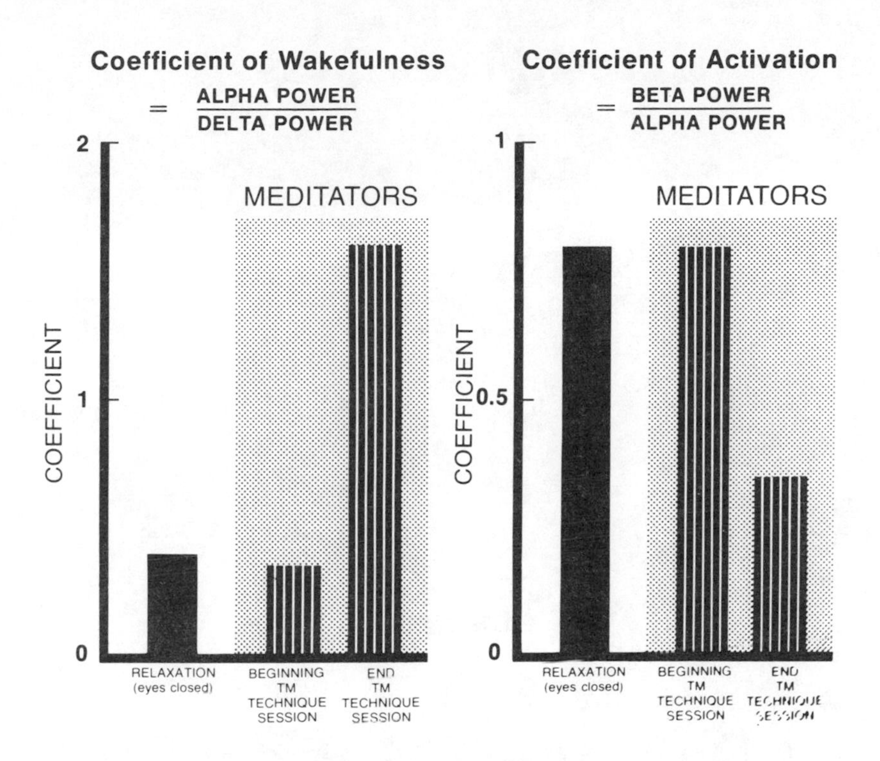

RESTFUL ALERTNESS: LIVELINESS IN REST

Finding: Electroencephalographic studies showed a shift in the distribution of brain wave power among the different frequency bands during the practice of the Transcendental Meditation technique. At the start of the TM technique session, meditators showed levels of wakefulness and activation typical of non-meditators simply relaxing with eyes closed. By the end of the TM technique session, however, the meditators showed heightened levels of wakefulness along with reduced levels of activation as measured by power ratios in the applicable EEG bands.

Interpretation: The rest produced by the Transcendental Meditation technique is not only physiologically superior to simple relaxation and sleep, but also results in better preparation for action, as shown by the increased degree of wakefulness indicated in the present study. The finding that this heightened wakefulness is achieved along with reduced activation validates subjective reports of full consciousness together with increased inner quietness and shows how the Transcendental Meditation technique cultures the mind to act from a 'lively field of silence.' It is this unique combination of deep rest with increased alertness that differentiates the Transcendental Meditation technique from other forms of wakeful relaxation, as well as dreaming and sleeping, and justifies the term 'fourth major state of consciousness.' The neurophysiological style of functioning that gives rise to this state of consciousness is responsible for all the benefits of the TM program shown in other scientific experiments.

Reference: Jean-Paul Banquet and Maurice Sailhan. "Analyse E.E.G. d'états de conscience induits et spontanés," *Revue D'Electroencephalographie et Neurophysiologie* 4 (France: 1974): 445–453.

Chapter 3

What Does the TM Program Do?

What are the benefits of the TM program?

Although we realize the body and mind are intimately connected, let us, for the sake of clarity, divide the benefits of the TM program into three categories—the mental benefits, the physical benefits, and the benefits that integrate both mind and body.

The TM program develops five fundamentals necessary for progress and success in life—Stability, Adaptability, Purification, Integration and Growth. During the course of this chapter will analyze how the Transcendental Meditation program fulfills each of these fundamentals on the level of the body (physiological), the mind (psychological), for the society as a whole (sociological), and for the environment (ecological).

Why don't you start by telling me the benefits the TM program has for the mind?

You will recall we said that rest is the basis of all our activity. This is because the clarity of our thinking depends on how rested we are. The success of our activity depends upon the quality of our thinking. Clear, direct thoughts lead spontaneously to effective, rewarding actions. Psychologists estimate that we use from 5–15% of our mental potential. This means we are only 5–15% effective—5–15% fulfilled.

If a machine functioned at only 5–15% efficiency, we would work diligently to improve it—yet many of us have had to accept limitations in our personal lives because there didn't seem to be any practical technique to improve our own mental efficiency.

During the TM technique we come into direct contact with the 85–95% of the mind we have not been using, and daily contact cultivates it—cultures it—until it is always available for our spontaneous use. The mind becomes expanded; our awareness increases.

Increased Intelligence Growth Rate

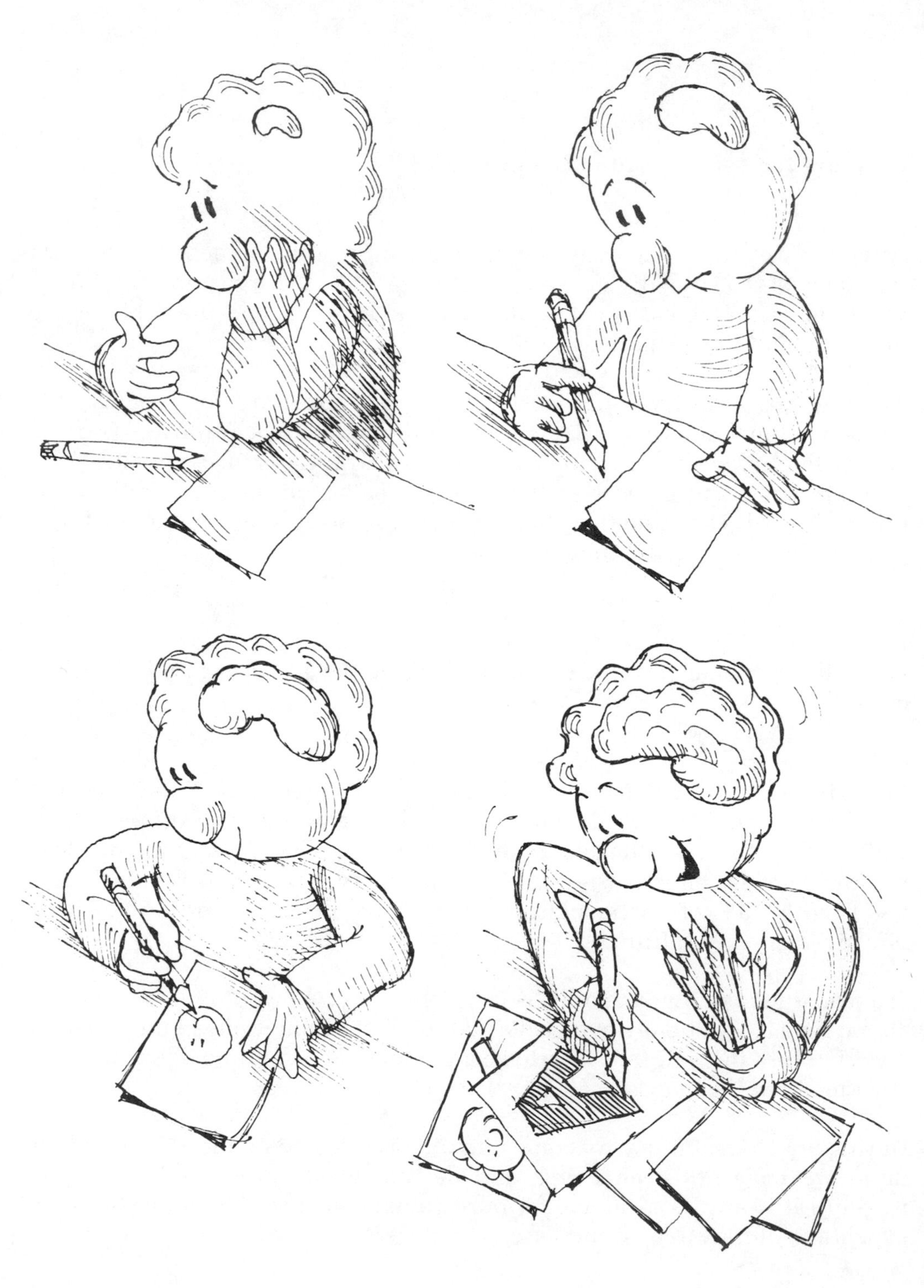

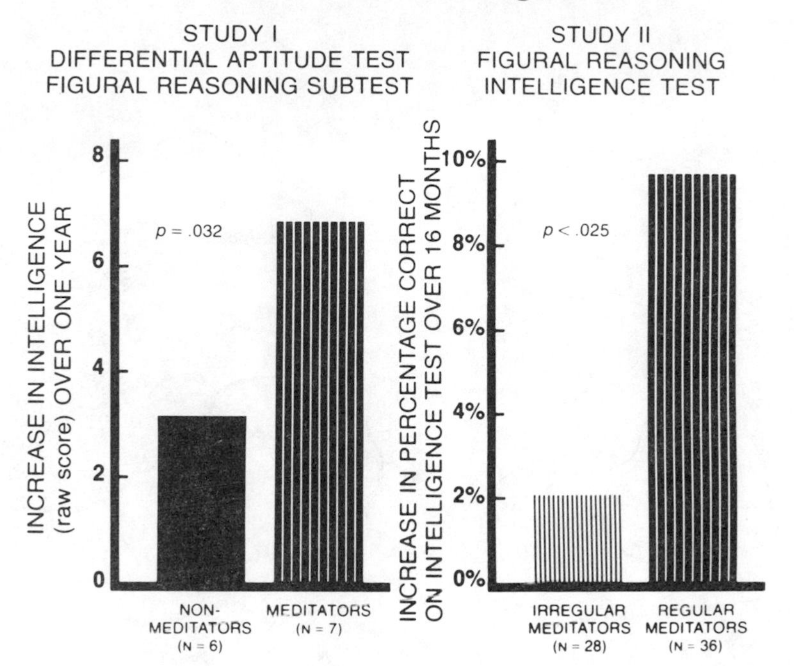

INCREASED INTELLIGENCE GROWTH RATE

Finding: The results of an initial study showed greater increase in intelligence among meditating high school students than among non-meditating controls. These results were confirmed in a second study that indicated that a group of university students and adults who practiced the Transcendental Meditation technique regularly (N = 36) increased significantly more in intelligence than those who did not meditate regularly (N = 28) over the 16-month period after they began the Transcendental Meditation technique ($p<.025$).

Interpretation: These findings indicate that the Transcendental Meditation program increases general fluid intelligence, which enables the meditator to respond to new situations with greater adaptability, creativity, and comprehension. After the age when intelligence growth is expected to reach a plateau, meditators continue to grow in greater degrees of creative intelligence.

First Reference: André S. Tjoa, "Some Evidence That the Transcendental Meditation Program Increases Intelligence and Reduces Neuroticisim as Measured by Psychological Tests," (University of Leiden, Leiden, the Netherlands).

Second Reference: André S. Tjoa, "Meditation, Neuroticism and Intelligence: A Follow Up," Gedrag, Tijdschrift voor Psychologie 3 (the Netherlands: 1975): 167–182.

Increased Learning Ability

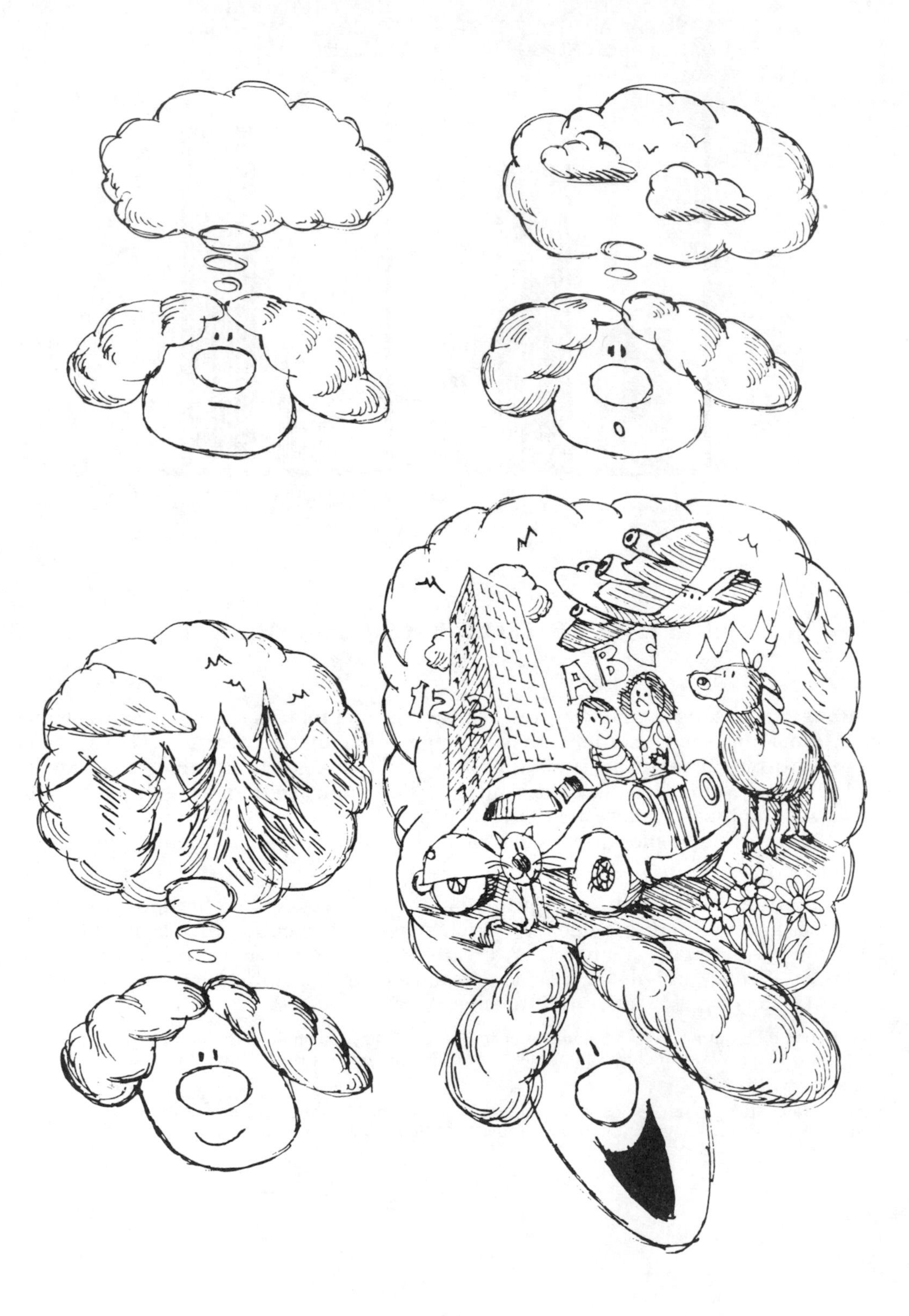

Recall Test Performance

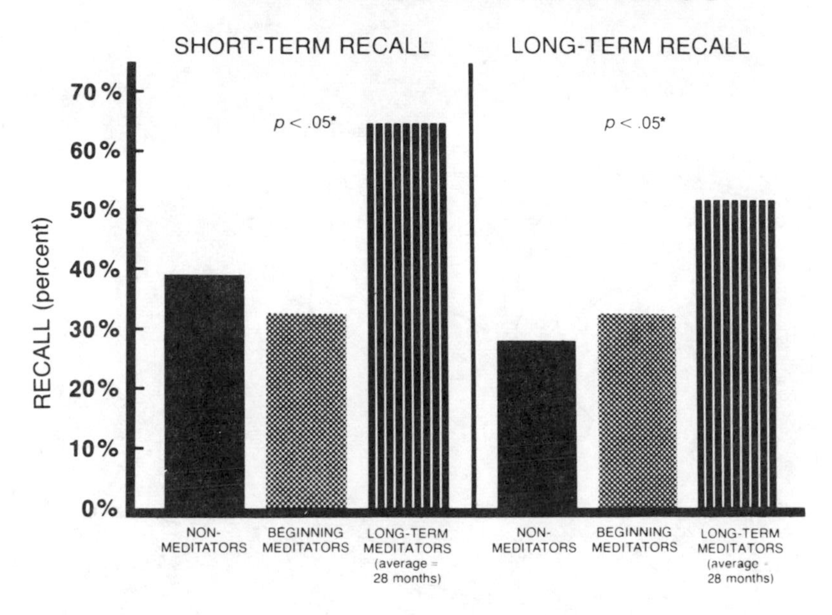

* Wilcoxon test comparing long-term meditators and nonmeditators.

INCREASED LEARNING ABILITY

Finding: Subjects who had practiced the Transcendental Meditation technique an average of 28 months performed better than non-meditators on short- and long-term recall tests as well as on tests of paired-associate learning. In addition, a trend towards progressive improvement in the long-term recall ability of meditators was found in comparing non-meditators, beginning meditators, and long-term meditators ($p<.01$, Kruskal-Wallis trend test).

Interpretation: These results indicate that the Transcendental Meditation program directly improves the ability to learn. This finding is even more significant in view of the common belief among psychologists that basic learning ability cannot be improved beyond late adolescence.

First Reference: Allen I. Abrams, "Paired-Associate Learning and Recall: A Pilot Study of the Transcendental Meditation Technique," (University of California, Berkeley, California, U.S.A.).

Second Reference: Donald E. Miskiman, "Performance in a Learning Task by Subjects Who Practice the Transcendental Meditation Technique," (University of Alberta, Edmonton, Alberta, Canada).

Increased Speed in Solving Problems Accurately

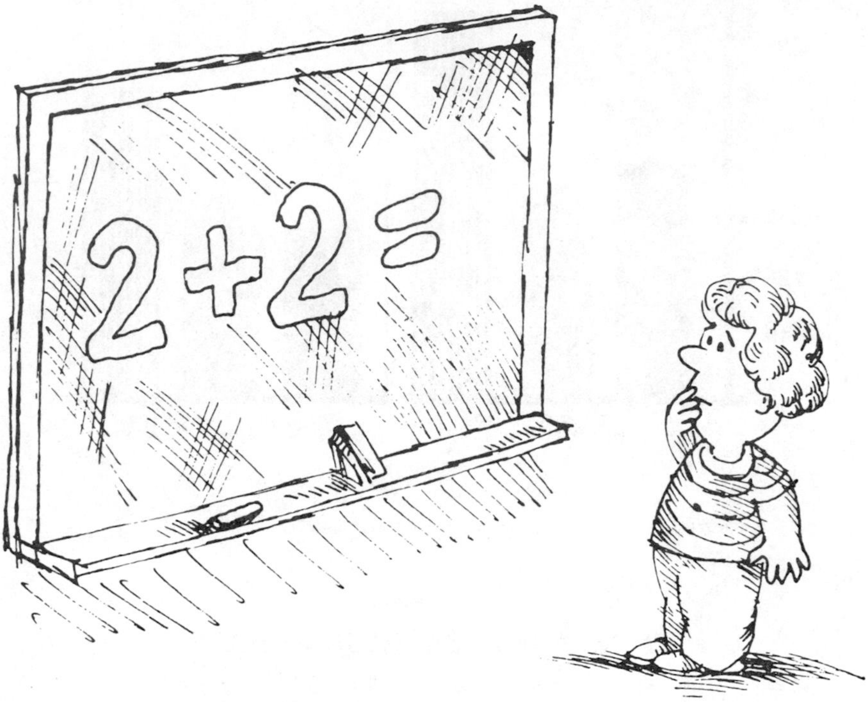

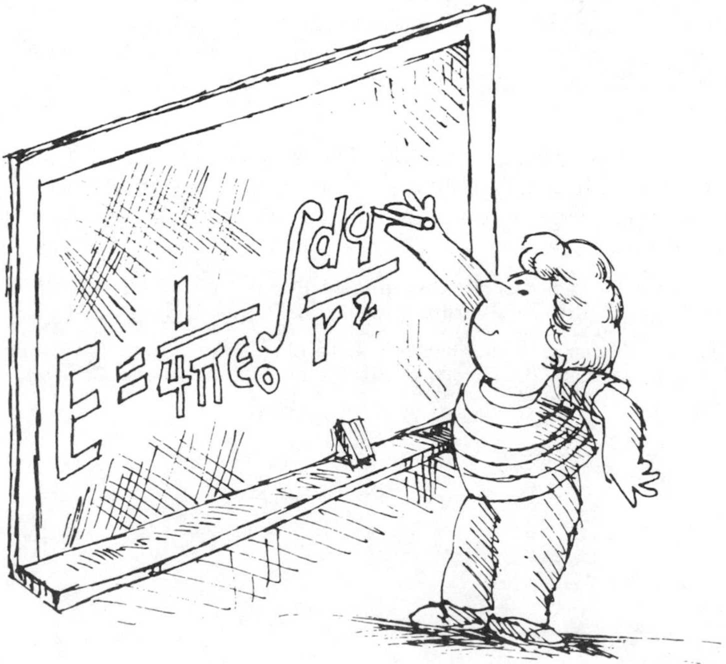

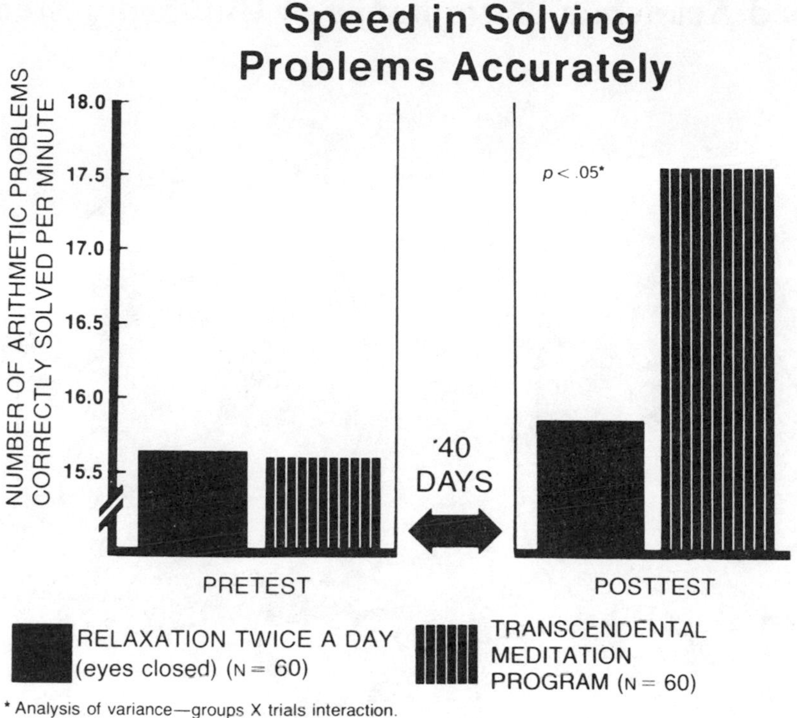

INCREASED ORDERLINESS OF THINKING

Finding: After beginning the practice of the Transcendental Meditation technique, meditators significantly increased their speed in solving arithmetic problems accurately. Two facts were found:

1. The efficiency of solving arithmetic problems increased in meditators who practiced the TM technique 20 minutes twice daily, compared with members of a control group who relaxed for an equivalent period of time twice daily.

2. A separate test of memory showed that improved organization of memory continued to stabilize even while the meditators were engaged in problem solving.

Interpretation: These results show that the Transcendental Meditation program increases the clarity and efficiency of conscious thought processes and at the same time improves the unconscious processes, leading to spontaneous and purposeful organization of thought. More orderly, purposeful, intelligent thought indicates unfoldment of full mental potential.

Reference: Donald E. Miskiman, "The Effect of the Transcendental Meditation Program on the Organization of Thinking and Recall (Secondary Organization)," (University of Alberta, Edmonton, Alberta, Canada).

Improved Academic Performance in University Students

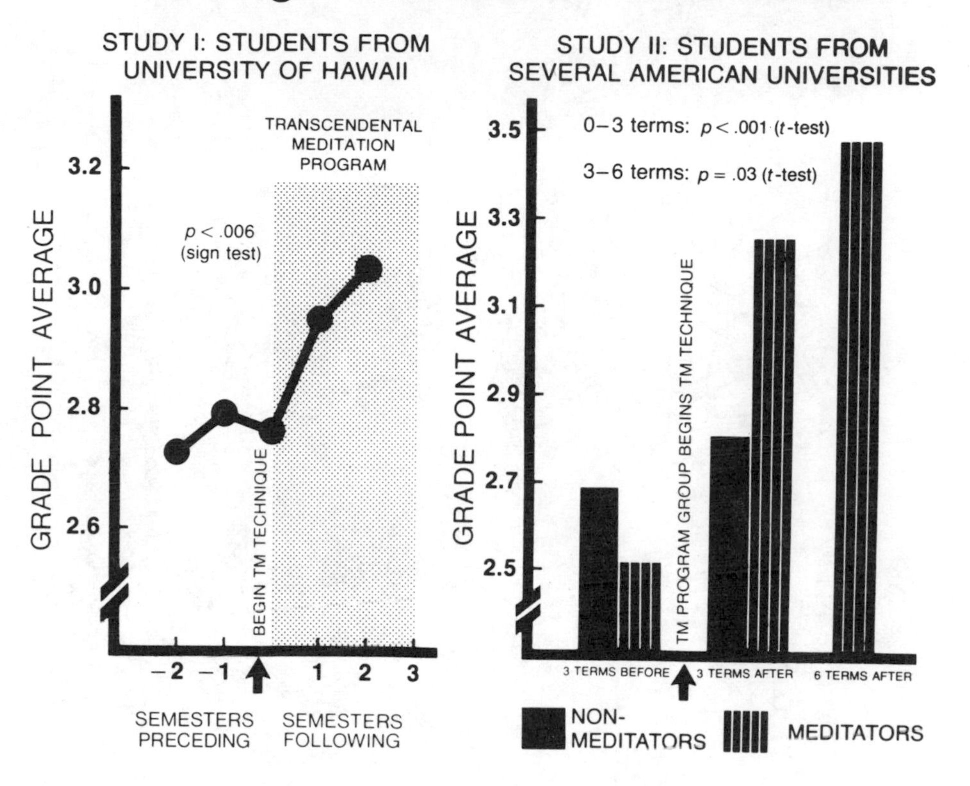

IMPROVED ACADEMIC PERFORMANCE UNIVERSITY STUDENTS

Finding: In two studies academic performance, as measured by grade point average (GPA), was shown to improve sharply after students began the Transcendental Meditation technique. Study I is a retrospective study of students at the University of Hawaii. The GPA for a minimum of two semesters before the students began the TM program was compared to their GPA for a minimum of one semester after they began the programme. Study II is a retrospective study comparing meditators with a matched control group of non-meditators.

Interpretation: The generalized improvement in neurophysiological and psychological functioning caused by the Transcendental Meditation technique naturally brings about improvement in a holistic measure of mental effectiveness, the ability to succeed in academic studies. Thus, the TM program is found to bring about a systematic development of creative intelligence.

First Reference: Study I: Roy W. Collier, "The Effect of Transcendental Meditation upon University Academic Attainment," (Paper presented at the Pacific Northwest Conference on Foreign Languages, Seattle, Washington, U.S.A.).

Second Reference: Study II: Dennis P. Heaton and David W. Orme-Johnson, "The Transcendental Meditation Program and Academic Achievement," (Maharishi International University, Fairfield, Iowa, U.S.A).

UNIVERSITY

You mean students can get better grades if they start the TM program?

Yes, that's been the experience. Thousands and thousands of students have found that they get better grades, enjoy school more, and have time left over for their friends.

And for those not in school?

Job performance improves.

Increased Productivity I

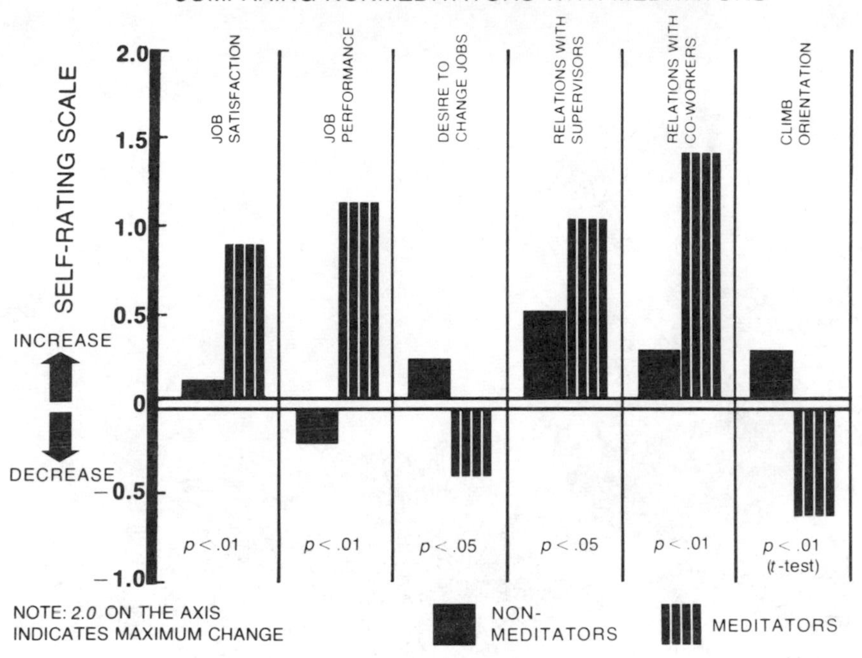

INCREASED PRODUCTIVITY I

Finding: In this study 42 students practicing the Transcendental Meditation technique an average of 11 months showed more job satisfaction, better job performance, more stability in their jobs, and better interpersonal relationships with their supervisors and co-workers than members of a control group. Whereas meditators reported that they felt less anxiety about promotion (shown by reduced climb orientation), their fellow employees saw them as moving ahead quickly.

Interpretation: At every level of organization performance improves when the members practice the Transcendental Meditation technique. Within the organizational structure meditators succeed more quickly and experience less anxiety. This indicates that a faster pace of progress is natural for persons practicing the TM technique.

Reference: David R. Frew, "Transcendental Meditation and Productivity," *Academy of Management Journal 17, no. 2* (U.S.A.: 1974): 362–368.

Increased Productivity II

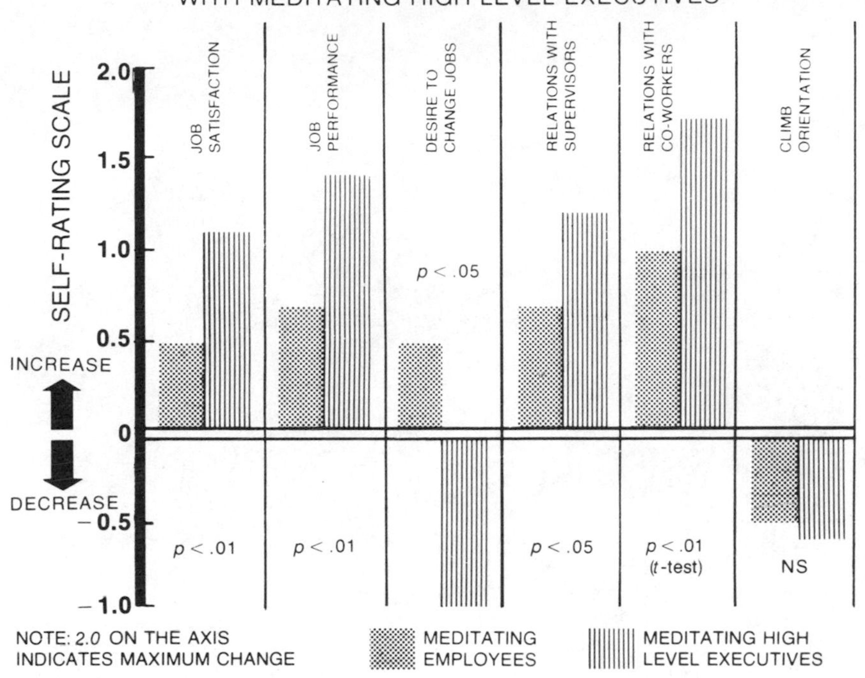

INCREASED PRODUCTIVITY II

Finding: Executives at higher levels of responsibility who practice the TM technique showed improved job performance, more job satisfaction, more stability in their jobs, and improved interpersonal relationships when compared with meditators at lower levels of organization.

Interpretation: The higher the individual's level of authority, the greater is the gain in productivity through the Transcendental Meditation program. The study indicates that although individuals at all levels of an organization gain in productivity through the Transcendental Meditation program, those at more responsible levels, where greater productivity is needed, find an even greater application for the increased creative intelligence systematically developed through the TM program.

Reference: David R. Frew, "Transcendental Meditation and Productivity," *Academy of Management Journal 17, no. 2* (U.S.A.: 1974): 362–368.

Improved Job Performance

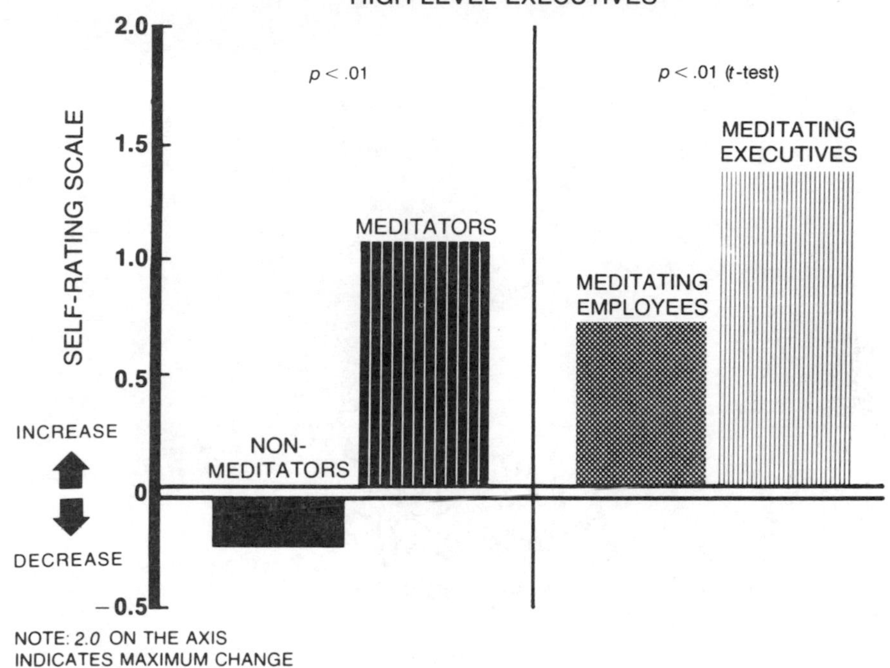

IMPROVED JOB PERFORMANCE

Finding: At all levels of organization those who practice the TM technique showed a significant increase in job performance compared with non-meditating controls. Meditating executives at higher levels of responsibility showed a comparatively greater increase in performance than those at less responsible levels.

Interpretation: Individuals at all levels of organization benefit from the development of creative intelligence through practice of the Transcendental Meditation technique. Executives at higher levels of responsibility, where greater creativity is demanded, find an even greater application for increased creative intelligence.

Reference: David R. Frew, "Transcendental Meditation and Productivity," *Academy of Management Journal 17, no. 2* (U.S.A.: 1974): 362–368.

And job satisfaction, too!

Increased Job Satisfaction

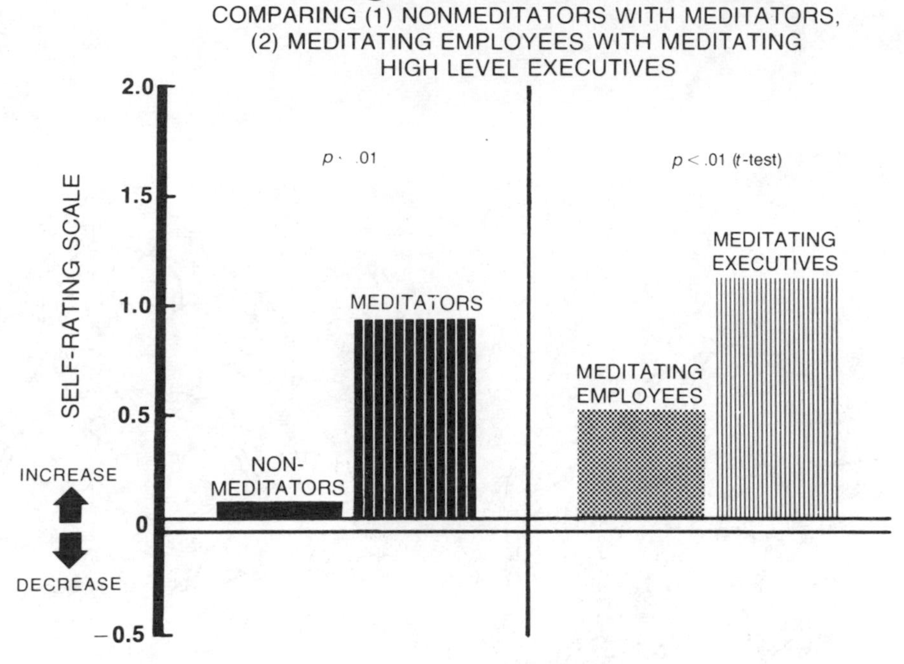

INCREASED JOB SATISFACTION

Finding: Forty-two subjects practicing the Transcendental Meditation technique an average of 11 months showed a greater increase in job satisfaction than did non-meditators over the same period of time. Executives at higher levels of management showed the greatest increase.

Interpretation: Because the Transcendental Meditation program improves job performance and thus increases the success of individuals at all levels of an organization, it brings increased job satisfaction.

Reference: David R. Frew, "Transcendental Meditation and Productivity," *Academy of Management Journal* 17, no. 2 (U.S.A.: 1974): 362–368.

Improved Relations with Supervisors

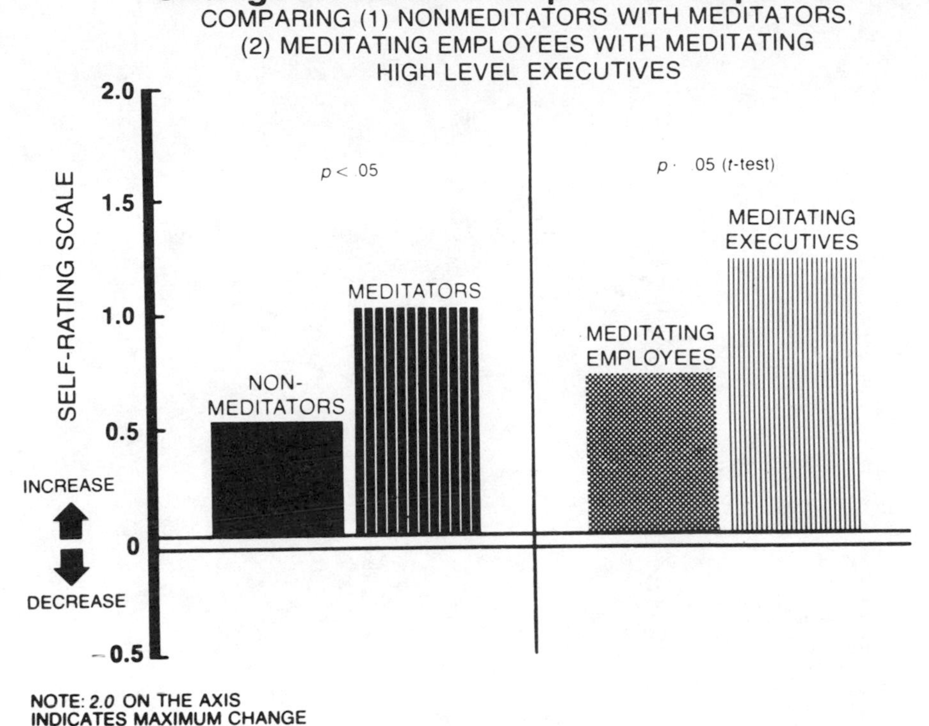

IMPROVED RELATIONSHIPS WITH SUPERVISORS

Finding: This study showed that the Transcendental Meditation program was effective in significantly improving employees' working relationships with their supervisors. Improvement was found to be comparatively greater for those at higher levels of organization.

Interpretation: The Transcendental Meditation program leads to more rewarding and productive interpersonal relationships in business by improving each individual's ability to do his job effectively and amiably while simultaneously increasing his stability and warmth of personality.

Reference: David R. Frew, "Transcendental Meditation and Productivity," *Academy of Management Journal* 17, no. 2 (U.S.A.: 1974): 362–368.

Improved Relations with Co-Workers

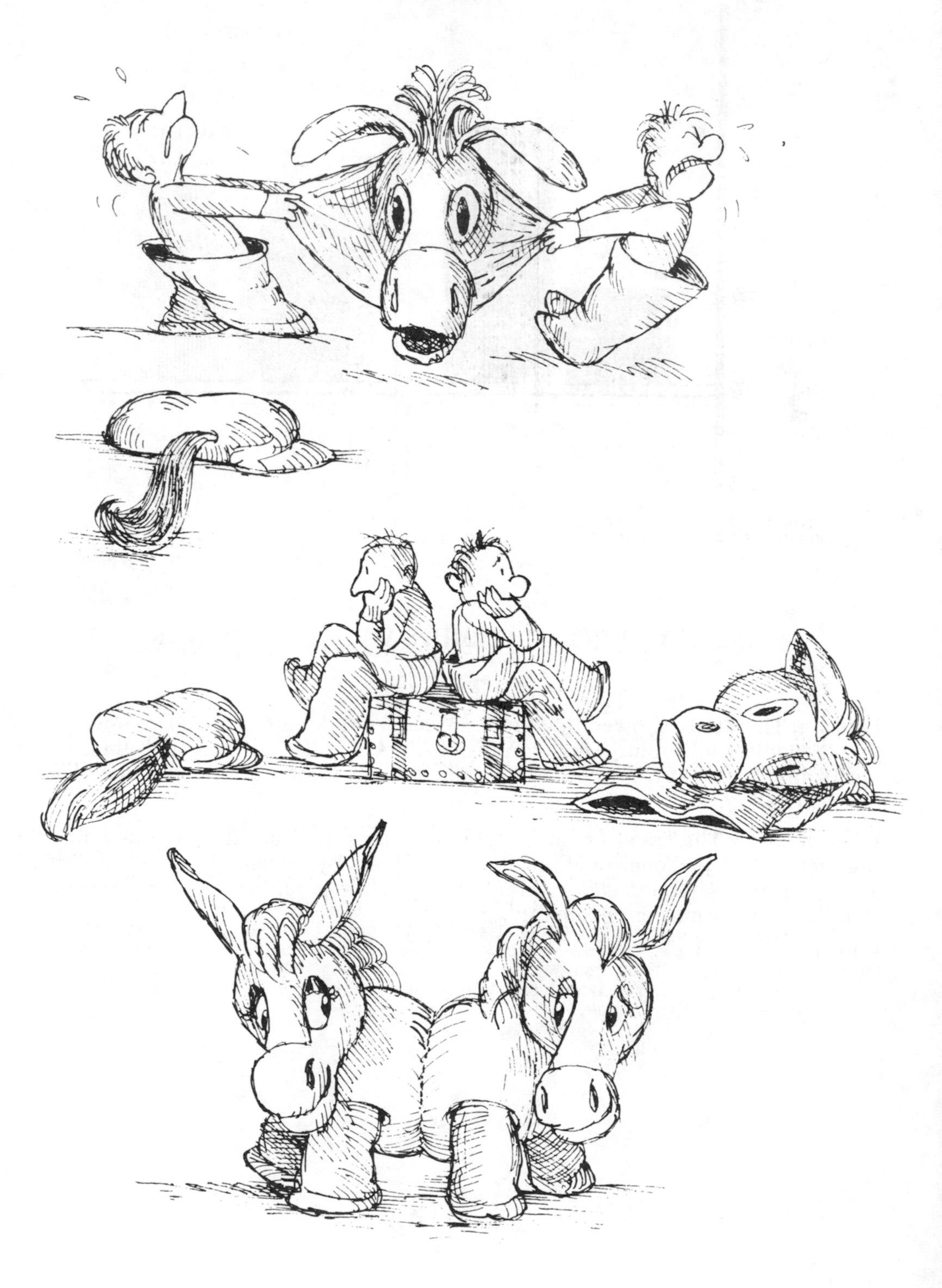

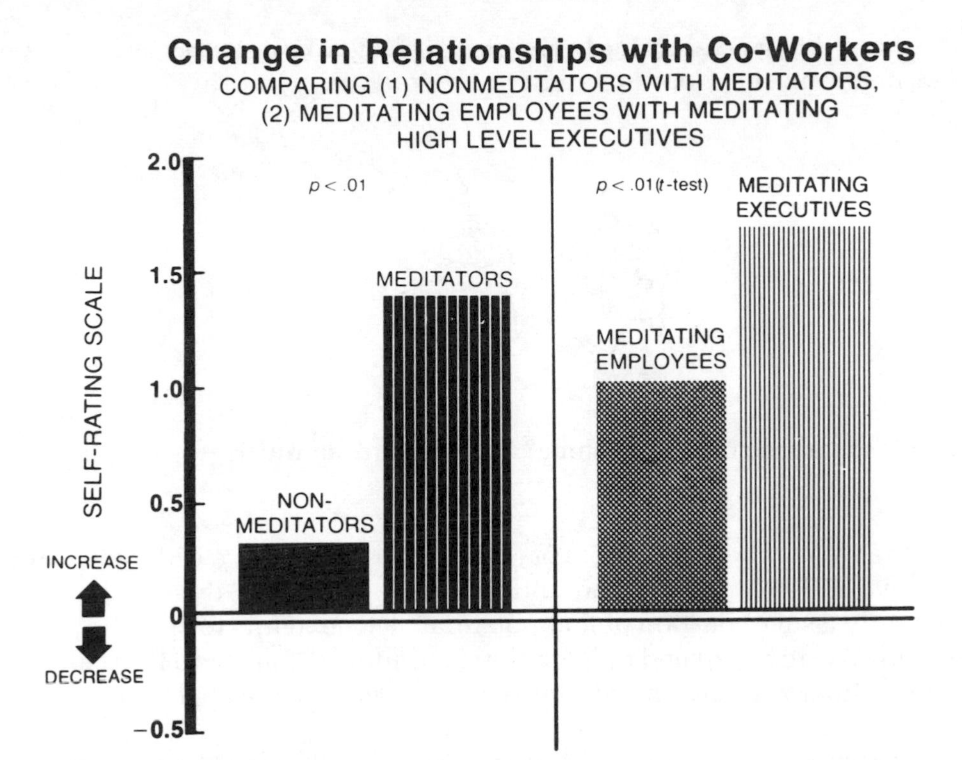

IMPROVED RELATIONSHIPS WITH CO-WORKERS

Finding: This study showed that working relationships with co-workers were significantly improved through practice of the Transcendental Meditation technique. This improvement was seen at both employee and executive levels.

Interpretation: This study shows that the Transcendental Meditation program brings about improved relationships at all levels of organization, indicating more harmonious interaction among different individuals working together within an organization. This may be seen as the sociological consequence of the effect of the Transcendental Meditation program on the individual—development of broadened awareness along with the ability of focus.

Reference: David R. Frew, "Transcendental Meditation and Productivity," *Academy of Management Journal* 17, no. 2 (U.S.A.: 1974): 362–368.

What is happening is really quite simple. Intelligence increases as a result of the TM program, therefore the ability to do *anything* improves.

But won't we all turn out the same? That would be dull!

No, not the same. The key word is *potential*. We each have a different potential, that is, different talents and abilities. The tragedy is that we have developed only a small portion of that potential. This extends to specific potential as well. We do not all end up with the same ability. Some will find calculus a breeze. Others will have no difficulty writing epic poems before breakfast.

The TM program brings a revolutionary concept into psychology—the fact that it is possible to greatly increase intelligence and creativity in adults. Now it is actually possible to become more intelligent as we acquire the experience of living.

With the TM technique our thinking becomes more flexible, more lively. After beginning the TM program, time ceases to be an enemy and becomes a friend. Before we started the program we thought, "Before long, I'll be five years older." But after starting the TM program we say, "In five years I'll have been practicing the TM technique five years longer." And we know that five years of the TM program means five years of increasing intelligence, expanding awareness, and growing stability.

So rather than becoming more and more the same, meditators become more and more different?

A useful analogy might be an orchard of trees, their roots deep in the same earth, yet their branches each yielding different fruit. We become more grounded in our common basis of creative intelligence, yet our expressions of that creative intelligence become stronger and more independent. And interestingly enough, that increased independence and individuality is enjoyed along with more and more harmony with others and with the environment.

Now let's go on to the physical benefits of the TM program.

The key word in discussing the TM program benefits to the body is *rest*. The body automatically heals and rejuvenates itself when allowed to rest. We experience this at night when we sleep: much of the tension and fatigue of the day is dissolved by that rest.

So if the body is rested during a night's sleep, why do we need the TM technique?

Although nightly sleep dissolves some fatigue and stress, the degree of rest is not complete enough to remove more deeply rooted stresses. To remove these stresses we need the deeper rest of the TM technique. This deeper rest twice daily also improves health, strengthens the body, and produces greater flexibility.

Rest

How can something be strong *and* flexible at the same time?

When speaking of the body, flexibility *means* strength. It's the old story of the willow and the oak tree. The willow bends to the strong wind, the oak tree tries to remain immovable. After the storm, the willow, flexible, stands; the oak, inflexible, has fallen.

Man has survived as the crown of physical creation because of his flexibility. A species survives if it can adapt to changing environmental conditions.

Life is full of change, jolts and sensations. If we are rigid, if we are not flexible, then these impulses can become intolerable bombardments, overloads to the system.

But if we can adapt to these experiences, they become part of the play of life.

This brings us to one of the Fundamentals of Progress, Adaptability.

ADAPTABILITY

PHYSIOLOGICAL ADAPTABILITY

The TRANSCENDENTAL MEDITATION technique provides coherent rest to the nervous system, as indicated by:

relaxation of the entire system:
- marked reduction in oxygen consumption
- natural change in breath rate and volume
- natural change in heart rate
- increased balance of autonomic nervous system

biochemical indication of relaxation
electrophysiological changes indicating relaxation

electroencephalographic changes indicating relaxation, as well as increased stability, orderliness, and coherence of brain activity

The daily cycle of deep rest provided by the alternation of the TRANSCENDENTAL MEDITATION technique and regular activity develops physiological adaptability—the ability of the nervous system to adjust to change with minimum consumption of energy—as indicated by: rapid recovery from stressful situations such as loud noises, exertion, sleep deprivation, and by increased vital capacity, increased cardiovascular efficiency, increased ease of breathing, normalization of weight, and improved athletic performance.

Furthermore, the greater adaptability through the TRANSCENDENTAL MEDITATION technique is indicated by: improved resistance to disease, less susceptibility to bronchial asthma, high blood pressure and insomnia.

These physiological changes account for the psychological changes.

PSYCHOLOGICAL ADAPTABILITY

Through the practice of the TRANSCENDENTAL MEDITATION technique, psychological adaptability—the ability of the mind to adjust to change for survival and progress—increases, as indicated by:

increased intelligence

broader comprehension and improved ability to focus attention

increased perceptual ability

increased learning ability

faster reactions

superior perceptual-motor performance

improved academic performance

increased self-sufficiency

improved organization of memory

increased speed in solving problems accurately

increased innovation

increased energy level

increased creativity

The TRANSCENDENTAL MEDITATION technique expands the conscious capacity of the mind through the experience of "profound wakefulness," "pure consciousness," or "unbounded awareness." An integrated, expanded consciousness is capable of broad vision and can at once intuit a more comprehensive range of any situation—the mind's adaptability increases in the service of existence and evolution.

These physiological and psychological changes account for the sociological changes.

SOCIOLOGICAL ADAPTABILITY

Through the TRANSCENDENTAL MEDITATION program, sociological adaptability—the ability of the members of society to change for maximum mutual benefit—increases, as indicated by:

more rewarding and productive interpersonal relationships in business

increased capacity for intimate contact

increased sociability

increased respect

flexibility in the application of one's own values

decreased rigidity

reduced social inadequacy

reduced social introversion

reduced antisocial behavior

reduced irritability

reduced use of alcohol and cigarettes

reduced use of nonprescribed drugs

reduced anxiety

increased tolerance

increased cordiality and good humor

These physiological, psychological, and sociological changes account for the ecological changes.

ECOLOGICAL ADAPTABILITY

It is our common experience that the homes of meditators are found to be more cordial, soothing, and harmonious, and in the homes of those nonmeditators where conflicts and dissension prevail, guests cannot avoid experiencing that discordant atmosphere.

Travelers likewise have experienced that their feelings change as they pass by certain villages. This is due to the quality of life in the village. For the same reason, international travelers have experienced that different countries project different feelings and this is clearly noticeable even while crossing the national borders.

From these common experiences it is obvious that the ecosphere shows a great range of adaptability and automatically adjusts to the influence created by man. It is fortunate for us who are concerned with the problems of ecology today that the scientific research on the TRANSCENDENTAL MEDITATION program has shown that life-supporting values increase in the meditator's physiology, psychology, and social life, as indicated by the scientific charts. These findings satisfy man's current search for an effective means to save and enrich the ecology because they show that the TRANSCENDENTAL MEDITATION program is the one thing that every man can do to produce life-supporting influences in his environment and radiate the influence of harmony in the ecosphere. The positive influence generated by the meditator enlivens and enriches the life-supporting quality of the ecosphere, thereby freeing it from the stress of negative influences, enabling it to be more refined and generous, and therefore more adaptable.

Isn't adaptability also a function of the mind?

Definitely. Expansion of the mind and flexibility of the body create true adaptability.

Can't we be too adaptable?

Stability is essential as well. An autumn leaf, drifting with the wind, is very adaptable—it goes wherever the wind sends it. Stability insures the fact that from one day to the next we continue to express the values we cherish and to uphold the responsibilities we have undertaken.

Stability is most certainly a Fundamental of Progress.

STABILITY

PHYSIOLOGICAL STABILITY

Through the practice of the TRANSCENDENTAL MEDITATION technique, physiological stability—the stable functioning of physiological processes—increases, as indicated by:

- stable state of rest:
  - metabolic stability
  - biochemical stability
  - electrophysiological stability
- stabilization of brain rhythms
- interhemispheric balance of brain activity
- habituation of stable, orderly brain functioning in activity
- improved physiology stabilized in activity:
  - increased cardiovascular efficiency
  - increased vital capacity
  - increased respiratory efficiency
  - increased metabolic stability
- rapid recovery of a stable physiological baseline:
  - improved recovery from exertion
  - increased autonomic stability
  - more effective interaction with the environment
- stabilized health:
  - improved resistance to disease
  - faster recovery from sleep deprivation
  - normalization of high blood pressure
  - relief from insomnia
  - beneficial effects on bronchial asthma
  - reduced use of alcohol and cigarettes
  - reduced use of nonprescribed drugs
  - normalization of weight

These physiological changes account for the psychological changes.

PSYCHOLOGICAL STABILITY

Through the practice of the TRANSCENDENTAL MEDITATION technique, psychological stability—maintenance of mental and emotional balance—increases, as indicated by:

increased emotional stability

decreased anxiety

reduced depression

reduced neuroticism

stronger intellect

stability of attention

increased inner control

increased self-confidence

stabilization of organized memory

increased individuality

increased self-actualization

increased self-esteem

Psychological stability develops automatically when the mind repeatedly gains and becomes habituated to its most stable status—pure consciousness—through the regular practice of the TRANSCENDENTAL MEDITATION technique. The mind and emotions become balanced through the experience of pure consciousness, resulting in purposeful thought and action, which stabilize the entire psychology.

These physiological and psychological changes account for the sociological changes.

SOCIOLOGICAL STABILITY

Through the practice of the TRANSCENDENTAL MEDITATION technique, sociological stability—stability of interpersonal relations—increases, as indicated by:

- improved relations between co-workers and supervisors
- growing stabilizing influences:
  - increased respect
  - increased cordiality
  - increased sociability
  - increased good humor
  - increased tolerance
  - increased tendency to see man as essentially good
  - increased job stability
- decreased disruptive influences:
  - decreased social inadequacy
  - decreased irritability
  - reduced use of nonprescribed drugs
  - stabilization of unstable members of society—more effective rehabilitation
- improved quality of city life—decreased crime rate
- developed capacity for warm interpersonal relationships

These physiological, psychological, and sociological changes account for the ecological changes.

ECOLOGICAL STABILITY

Through the practice of the TRANSCENDENTAL MEDITATION technique, the meditator grows in physiological, psychological, and sociological stability. As man is the most influential member of the environment, when he grows in stability, naturally he radiates the influence of stability around him, securing balance and intensifying harmony in the environment. This is how the TRANSCENDENTAL MEDITATION program is a direct means of promoting ecological stability.

- increased physiological stability:
  - increased stability of the autonomic nervous system
  - stable state of rest
  - improved physiology stabilized
  - stabilized health
- increased psychological stability:
  - increased emotional stability
  - increased inner control
  - increased self-regard and self-confidence
  - decreased anxiety
  - decreased depression
  - decreased neuroticism
- increased sociological stability:
  - increased job stability
  - stability of interpersonal relationships
  - reduced use of alcohol and cigarettes
  - reduced use of nonprescribed drugs
  - reduced crime rate
  - more effective rehabilitation

The TM program makes the nervous system more stable.

Increased Autonomic Stability

Spontaneous Skin Resistance Responses

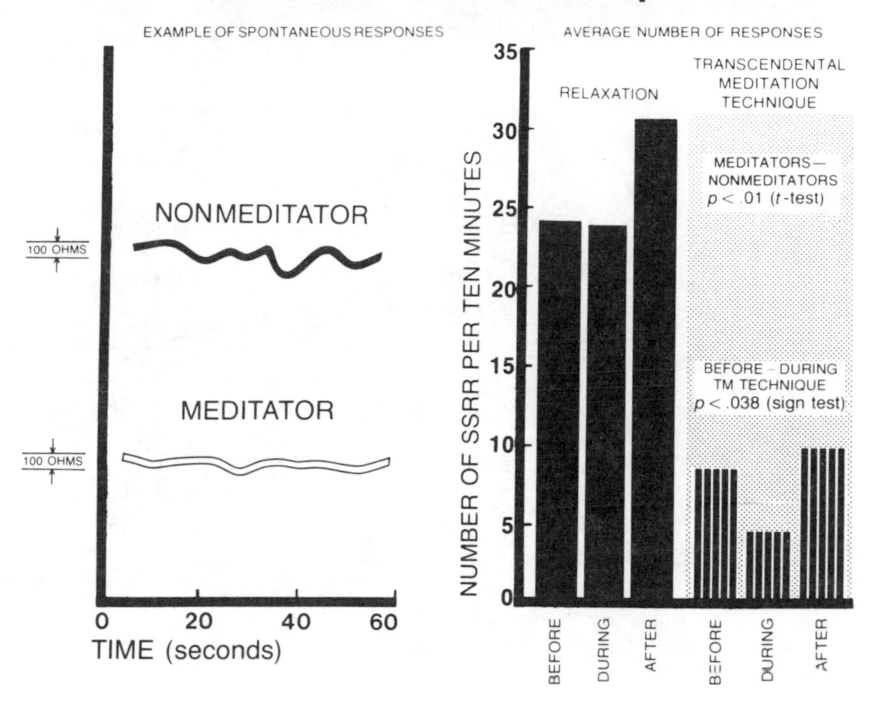

INCREASED AUTONOMIC STABILITY

Finding: Subjects practicing the Transcendental Meditation technique were found to have fewer spontaneous skin resistance responses (SSRR) than non-meditating control subjects ($p<.01$), indicating greater stability in the autonomic nervous system.

Interpretation: The Transcendental Meditation technique stabilizes the nervous system, as shown by fewer spontaneous skin resistance responses. This stability continues to be maintained after practice of the technique. Psychophysiologists have generally shown that a condition of fewer skin resistance responses is highly correlated with greater resistance to environmental stress, psychosomatic disease, and behavioral instability, as well as with greater efficiency in the activity of the nervous system. The Transcendental Meditation technique reduces the 'noise level' of the nervous system and thereby frees more energy for perception, thought, and purposeful activity.

Reference: David W. Orme-Johnson, "Autonomic Stability and Transcendental Meditation," *Psychosomatic Medicine* 35, no. 4 (U.S.A.: 1973): 341–349.

FOR SALE

The TM program also improves adaptability and makes us more accurate and flexible in our response to the environment.

Faster Reaction Time

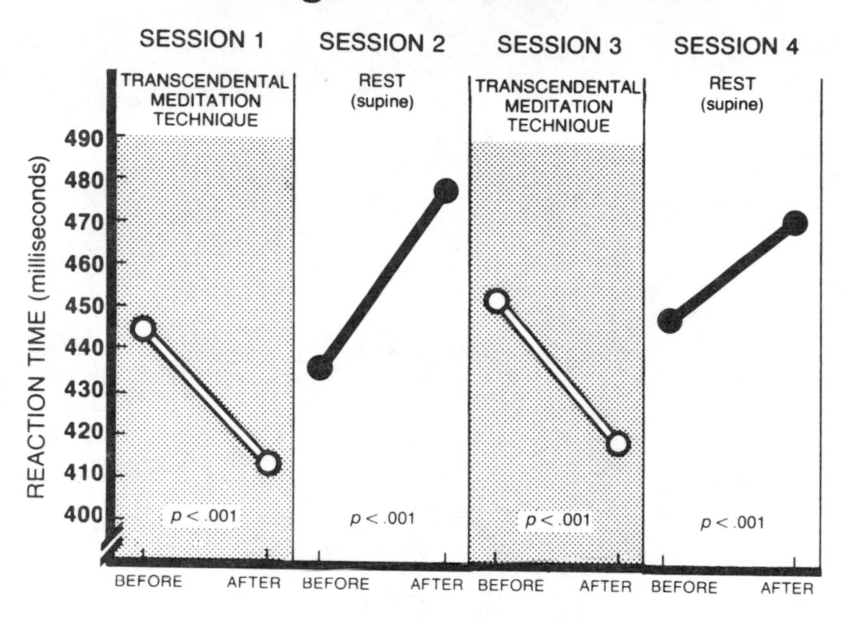

FASTER REACTIONS

Finding: Twenty-five subjects were measured over four different sessions of either practicing the Transcendental Meditation technique or relaxing. The Transcendental Meditation technique was consistently found to speed up reactions, whereas resting in a supine position resulted in a slowing of reactions.

Interpretation: The Transcendental Meditation technique speeds up reactions, indicating increased alertness, improved coordination of mind and body, and improved efficiency in perception and performance. This experiment also shows that the TM technique results in significantly more freshness and alertness than is achieved by merely lying down. The state produced by the TM technique is a superior form of coherent deep rest.

First Reference: David W. Orme-Johnson, David Kolb, and J. Russell Hebert, "An Experimental Analysis of the Effects of the Transcendental Meditation Technique on Reaction Time" (Maharishi International University, Fairfield, Iowa, U.S.A.).

Second Reference: Robert Shaw and David Kolb, "Reaction Time Following the Transcendental Meditation Technique," (University of Texas at Austin, Austin, Texas, U.S.A.).

Third Reference: Stuart Appelle and Lawrence Oswald, "Simple Reaction Time as a Function of Alertness and Prior Mental Activity," *Perceptual and Motor Skills 38* (U.S.A.: 1974): 1263–1268.

Superior Perceptual-Motor Performance

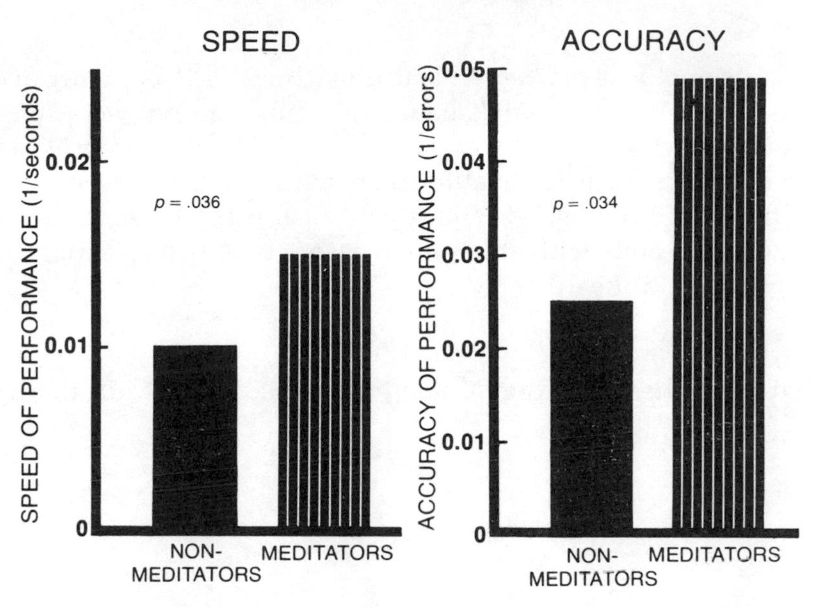

SUPERIOR PERCEPTUAL-MOTOR PERFORMANCE

Finding: Subjects who practice the Transcendental Meditation technique performed faster and more accurately on a complex perceptual-motor test (Mirror Star-Tracing Test). The test measures the ability to trace a pattern while watching its reflection in a mirror without becoming disoriented.

Interpretation: Performance as measured by this test is relevant to such tasks as driving a car, hitting a target, and performing in many different sports. The superior performance of meditators indicates that the Transcendental Meditation program produces greater coordination between mind and body, greater flexibility, increased perceptual awareness, superior resistance to disorientation, greater efficiency, and improved neuromuscular integration.

Reference: Karen S. Blasdell, "The Effects of the Transcendental Meditation Technique upon a Complex Perceptual-Motor Task," (University of California, Los Angeles, California, U.S.A.).

You mentioned health?

The first thing the doctor says when he learns of illness is "Get plenty of rest." This is because he knows the body's natural healing and rejuvenating qualities are most active when the body is at rest. The TM technique provides the body with an excellent basis for health because it provides even deeper rest than sleep. The word "disease" is significant. It means dis-ease—a lack of ease. TM provides the body with unbounded ease—twice a day. This removes the cause of physical ill health.

We know that heart disease is the number one cause of death in the United States.

Rest

Change in Heart Rate

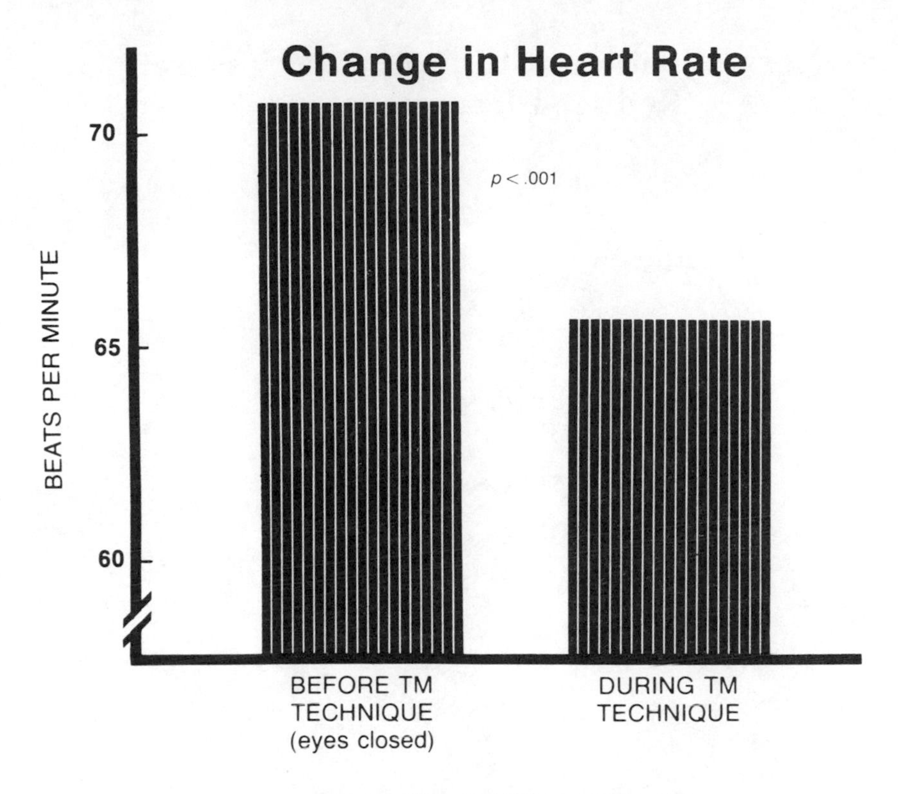

CHANGE IN HEART RATE

Finding: Heart rate was recorded by electrocardiogram in 11 long-term meditators (average time meditating 25 months, average age 23 years). During the Transcendental Meditation technique the average decrease in heart rate was five beats per minute compared with the rate before practice of the technique (sitting with eyes closed).

Interpretation: When taken together with additional data from the same study, this finding suggests that cardiac output also decreases, implying a reduction in the work load of the heart during the Transcendental Meditation technique.

Reference: Robert Keith Wallace, "The Physiological Effects of Transcendental Meditation: A Proposed Fourth Major State of Consciousness," (Ph.D. Thesis, Department of Physiology, University of California, Los Angeles, California, U.S.A., 1970).

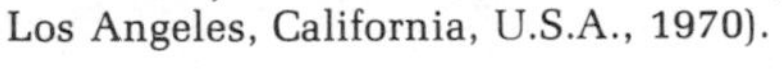

This chart shows that the heart rate decreases during the TM technique. This means that the TM program gives the heart a significant rest—twice daily.

Also, the TM program normalizes blood pressure.

Normalization of High Blood Pressure: Reduced Hypertension

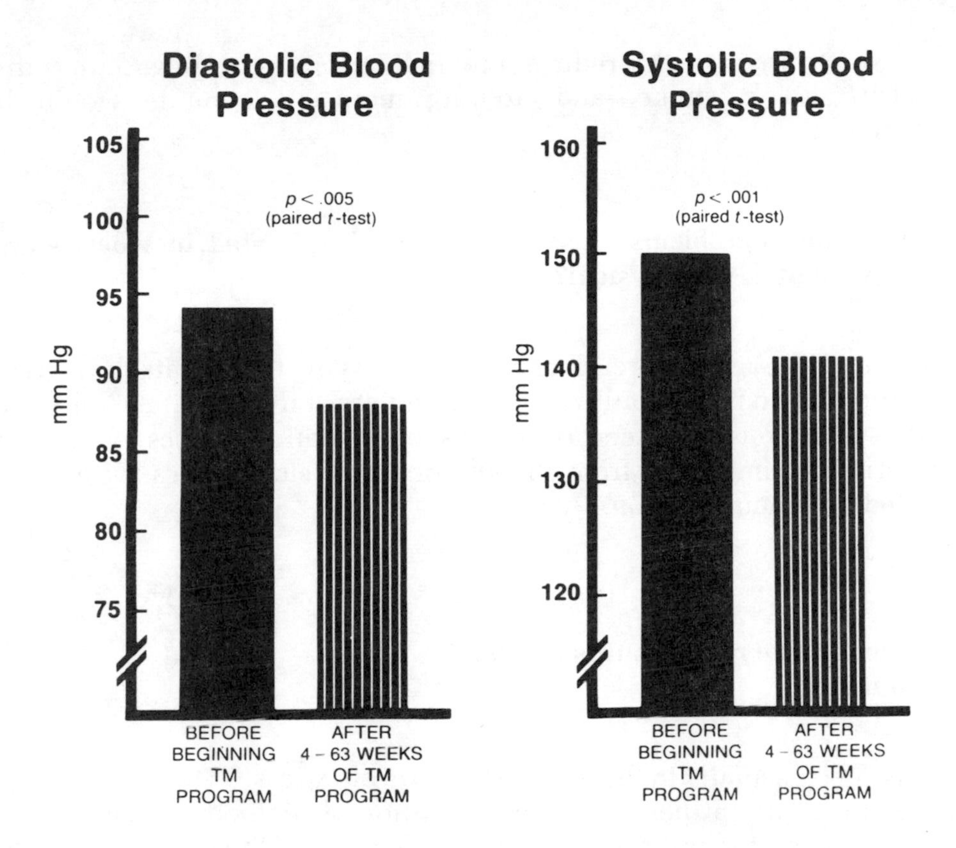

NORMALIZATION OF HIGH BLOOD PRESSURE

Finding: Systolic and diastolic arterial blood pressures were recorded 1,119 times in 22 hypertensive patients before and after they began the Transcendental Meditation program. The decreases in blood pressure after patients began practicing the Transcendental Meditation technique were statistically significant.

Interpretation: These findings indicate that the Transcendental Meditation program is useful and effective as an adjunct in the treatment of high blood pressure. In the U.S.A. alone essential hypertension affects over 23 million citizens, including one out of every three adult males. High blood pressure increases the risk of disease and death due to heart attack, stroke, and damage to vital organs. Autonomic liability (instability) has been shown to be a precursor to hypertension. The Transcendental Meditation program promotes autonomic stability and may be important in both the treatment of hypertension and the prevention of cardiovascular disease. Note: People under the care of a physician should go by their physician's advice in coordinating participation in the TM program with ongoing medical care and medication.

First Reference: Herbert Benson and Robert Keith Wallace, "Decreased Blood Pressure in Hypertensive Subjects Who Practiced Meditation," Supplement II to *Circulation* 45 and 46 (U.S.A.: 1972).

Second Reference: Barry Blackwell, Irwin Hanenson, Saul Bloomfield, Herbert Magenheim, Sanford Nidich, and Peter Gartside, "Effects of Transcendental Meditation on Blood Pressure: A Controlled Pilot Experiment," *Journal of Psychosomatic Medicine* 37, (U.S.A.: 1975): 86.

If the TM program could reduce the incidence of cardiovascular disease—heart attack, stroke—and nothing more, its benefits would be overwhelming.

Aren't many heart problems caused, or at least complicated, by worry—and isn't worry mental, not physical?

Yes, and yes. Here again we reach an impasse in trying to separate the activity of the mind and body. Not only does the mind affect the "obvious" physical ailments—heart trouble, ulcers, asthma, psychosomatic illnesses—but medical authorities estimate that from 60–90% of *all* physical illness is caused or aggravated by mental tension.

The TM technique removes this tension from the mind?

The "tension" is actually in the body in the form of "stress." The quality of our thinking is directly influenced by the condition of the body. If the body is rested and at ease, the mind is relaxed and effective. If the body is tired and stressed, the mind is worried and tense.

It's another of those vicious circles: the more stress we have, the more we get.

Yes, and it works both ways. Not only does the TM program remove the stress that is in the body, it also prevents new stress from building up. And the less stress we have, the less stress we get. A clear mind perceives situations more fully, and the more we see, the less upsetting life is.

How does that work?

I'm sure at one time or another we've walked into a dark room and—even if it was in our own home—experienced fear. Yet, as soon as the light was turned on we could see that everything was all right. As our awareness expanded to include the whole room, our fear vanished.

Many of the situations we perceive as stressful are merely a reflection of our own limited perception—our own narrowness of vision.

What do you mean by "stress"?

Stress is any chemical or physical abnormality in the body, in the nervous system. It is caused by overload. When some physical or emotional pressure of experience distorts the system, that overload is stress. When the stresses are too deeply rooted or too numerous to be relieved by a good night's sleep, then they accumulate and we become increasingly ineffective in our activity.

Then stress must interfere with everything we do!

Yes, but consider the consequences of eliminating stress stored in the nervous system. When we're stressed, we see things negatively; when we're refreshed and rested, we perceive positively. When the nervous system is strained and tired, our activity seems fruitless and futile; when our mind is clear and alert, we can make the best use of everything around us without even trying.

When we're hassled and upset, the tiniest irritation can make it impossible to communicate. How many times have you felt that if a situation didn't upset you so much, it would be *easy* to do the right thing?

More than I care to remember.

This is because stress keeps building up in our lives and overshadows the normal, easy enjoyment of life that we *should* be experiencing. When stresses are dissolved by the deep rest of the TM technique, the nervous system is allowed to function in a holistic and balanced way. Then all our thoughts and actions are creative and successful. And all of our relationships are natural and rewarding.

Will the TM program remove everybody's inhibitions?

If by inhibitions you mean obstacles that keep us from functioning freely, then you're talking about stress. The TM program will definitely eliminate stress.

But aren't some inhibitions good?

Manners are good. Inhibitions are not good. Inhibitions are involuntary. We have no *choice*. They are imprisoning. Good manners are a matter of choice. We follow certain impulses and don't follow others. Right and moral action is the natural result of a stress-free nervous system.

So these stresses distort perception and inhibit expression.

Yes.

Increased Perceptual Ability: Auditory Discrimination

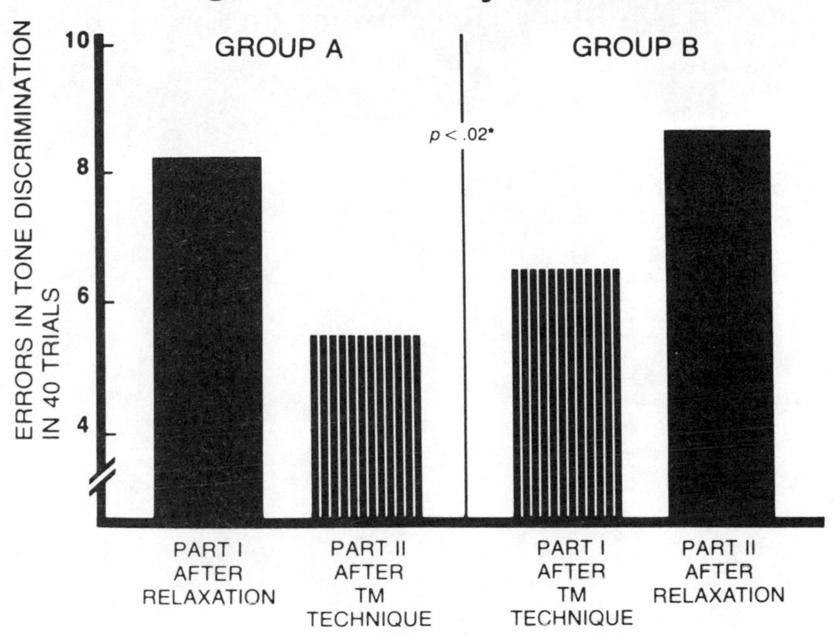

INCREASED PERCEPTUAL ABILITY

Finding: The ability of meditators to discriminate small differences in the length of auditory tones was significantly better ($p<.02$) after practicing the Transcendental Meditation technique than after simply sitting with eyes closed. Experimental group A relaxed with eyes closed first, then meditated. Experimental group B meditated, then relaxed with eyes closed. In both cases performance immediately following the Transcendental Meditation technique was superior to that immediately following relaxation.

Interpretation: This indicates an increased refinement of perception following the TM technique and suggests that the deep rest produced by the technique reduces the 'noise' in the perceptual system, resulting in improved information-processing capabilities. This conclusion is supported by the finding that reactions are also faster after the Transcendental Meditation technique than after simply lying down with eyes closed. The Transcendental Meditation technique improves the 'signal-to-noise' ratio of the nervous system, resulting in more sensitive perceptions.

Reference: Michael Pirot, "The Effects of the Transcendental Meditation Technique upon Auditory Discrimination," (University of Victoria, Victoria, British Columbia, Canada).

As the regular practice of the Transcendental Meditation technique continues, we notice an increasing sense of freedom. Our thoughts and feelings are more freely and clearly expressed. This process of releasing stress and tension in a totally effortless way brings us to another Fundamental of Progress fulfilled by the TM program, Purification.

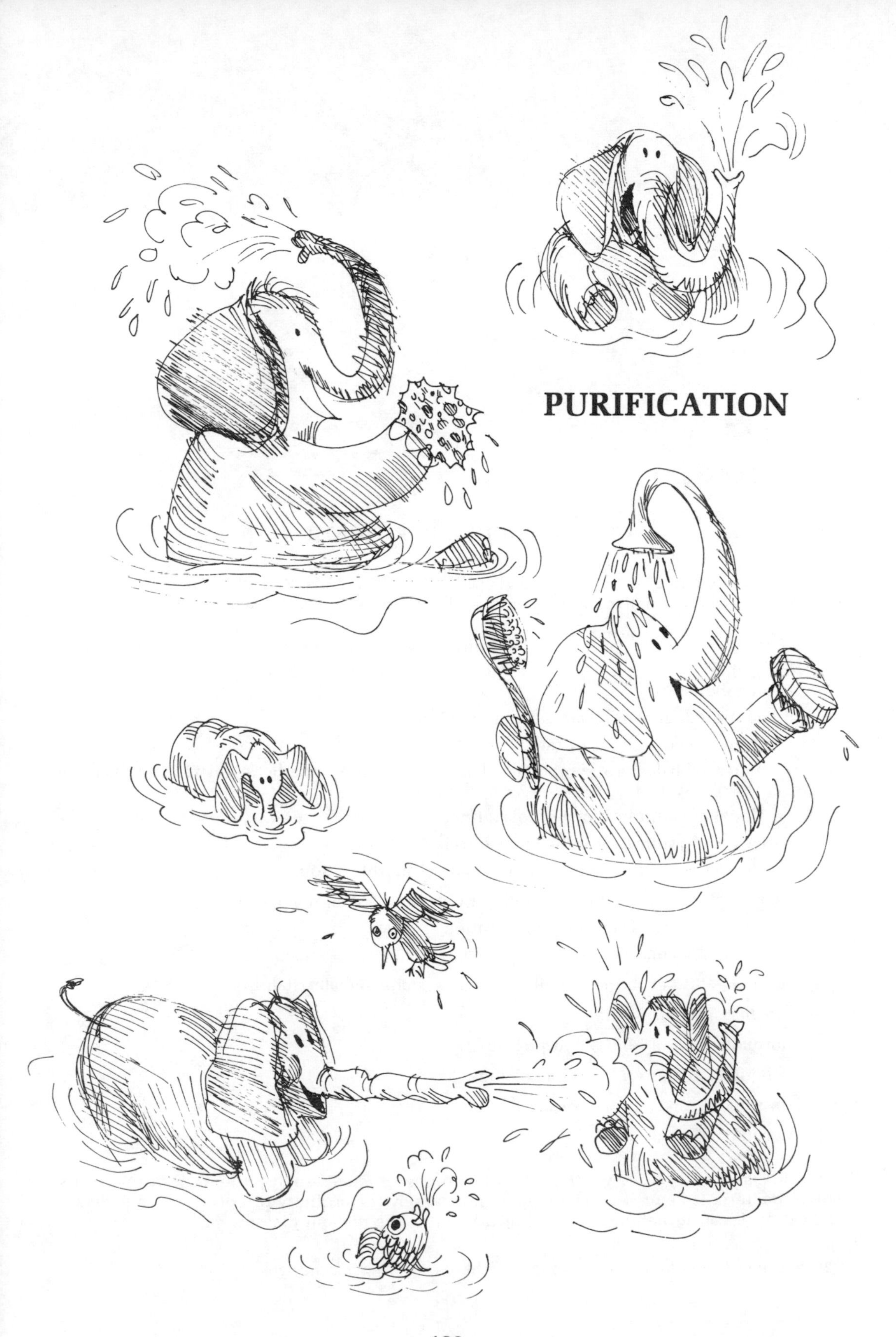

PURIFICATION

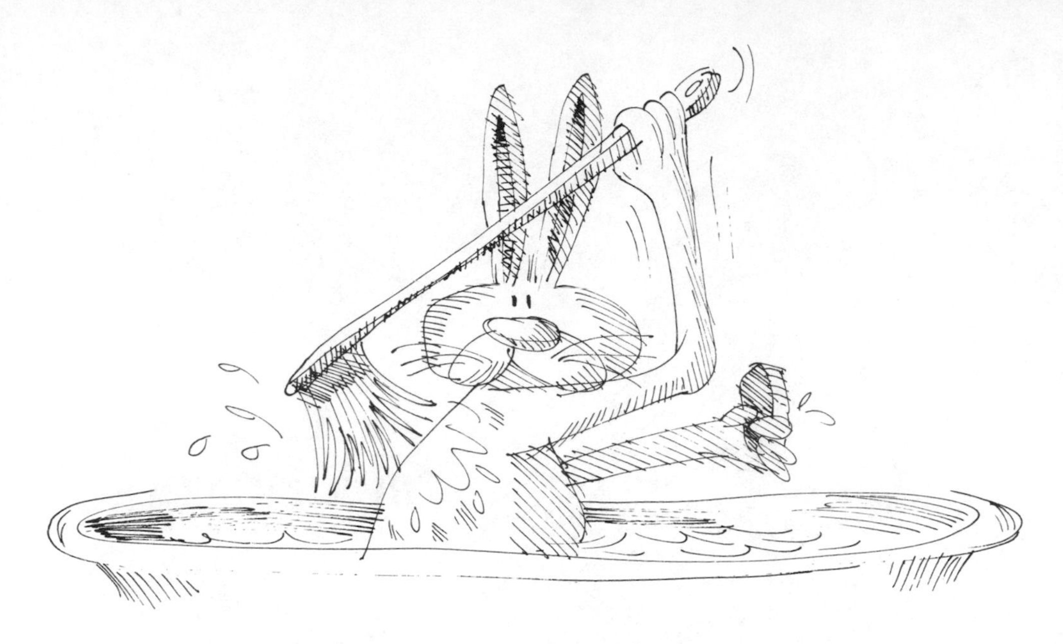

PHYSIOLOGICAL PURIFICATION

Through the practice of the TRANSCENDENTAL MEDITATION technique, physiological purification—the normalization of the physiology—increases, as indicated by:

- increased efficiency of the body's natural processes of purification by providing a deep state of rest:
  - metabolic rest
  - natural change in breath rate and volume
  - natural change in heart rate
  - increased balance of sympathetic (active) and parasympathetic (restful) aspects of the nervous system
  - biochemical indications of relaxation
  - electrophysiological indications of relaxation
  - electroencephalographic changes indicating relaxation
- increased efficiency of the purifying processes of sleeping and dreaming:
  - faster recovery from sleep deprivation
  - reduced insomnia
- normalization of the autonomic nervous system—greater stability
- biochemical purification
- normalization of high blood pressure
- beneficial effects on bronchial asthma
- improved resistance to disease
- normalization of weight

The TRANSCENDENTAL MEDITATION technique produces such profound rest that it dissolves deep-rooted stresses that are not eliminated by the ordinary rest of sleep. This physiological purification stabilizes normal health and helps prevent disease.

These physiological changes account for the psychological changes.

PSYCHOLOGICAL PURIFICATION

Through the practice of the TRANSCENDENTAL MEDITATION technique, psychological purification—reduction of negativity and increased positivity in thinking, understanding, and emotions—increases, as indicated by:

- increased positive qualities:
  - increased emotional stability
  - increased spontaneity
  - increased self-actualization
  - increased self-confidence and naturalness
  - increased self-esteem
  - increased innovation
  - increased individuality
  - increased tolerance
  - increased positive behavior
  - increased intelligence
  - increased orderliness of thinking
- reduced negative traits:
  - decreased anxiety
  - decreased depression
  - decreased personal inadequacy and rigidity
  - decreased neurosis

The TRANSCENDENTAL MEDITATION program does not directly concern itself with problems or negativity of any kind. The technique allows the mind to effortlessly experience pure consciousness, the supreme value of psychological purification. As pure consciousness is the basis of all progress and as this is brought about by the process of physiological and psychological purification, it is obvious that purification is essential to progress—a natural means of purification is invariably a natural means to progress.

These physiological and psychological changes account for the sociological changes.

SOCIOLOGICAL PURIFICATION

Through the practice of the TRANSCENDENTAL MEDITATION technique, sociological purification—the reduction of negativity in society—increases, as indicated by:

decreased crime rate

decreased antisocial tendencies resulting in more effective rehabilitation

decreased use of nonprescribed drugs

reduced use of alcohol and cigarettes

increased sociability

increased tolerance

increased good humor

increased cordiality

increased tendency to view man as essentially good

developed capacity for warm interpersonal relationships

broadened comprehension

increased comprehension of the consequences of one's behavior

Considering the phenomenon of sociological purification objectively, as members of society rise to more comprehensive awareness through the physiological and psychological purification brought about by the TRANSCENDENTAL MEDITATION program, the institutions of social purification, such as law enforcement agencies and the judiciary, prisons and rehabilitation centers, educational systems, and hospitals spontaneously fulfill their objectives. The activities of these organizations will become more effective as their members rise to full potential.

These physiological, psychological, and sociological changes account for the ecological changes.

ECOLOGICAL PURIFICATION

Through the TRANSCENDENTAL MEDITATION program, ecological purification increases—wholeness of ecological values blossoms—harmony becomes more and more evident in the midst of diversity. This is on the basis of the total effect of the practice resulting in:

reduced negativity

more harmonious interaction with the environment

Considering the phenomenon of ecological purification objectively, mechanisms of self-purification are found in the ecosystem (e.g., decomposers and scavengers) as in the individual (e.g., the immune system—the body's ability to resist disease). These intrinsic purifying mechanisms and their balance in nature can be overwhelmed by the negative influence that man may produce due to his lack of total vision, his short-sightedness and selfishness, and even by the undue aggression coming from his stressed life. The TRANSCENDENTAL MEDITATION program, developing fullness in man, has the ability to promote life-supporting influences and thereby naturally maintain ecological purification, eliminating the very basis of all pollution.

Any scientific proof?

One measure of how well we function is the level of anxiety—low anxiety means a feeling of inner security that enables us to interact with our environment in a harmonious way. During the TM technique, anxiety is greatly reduced.

Biochemical Changes: Blood Lactate

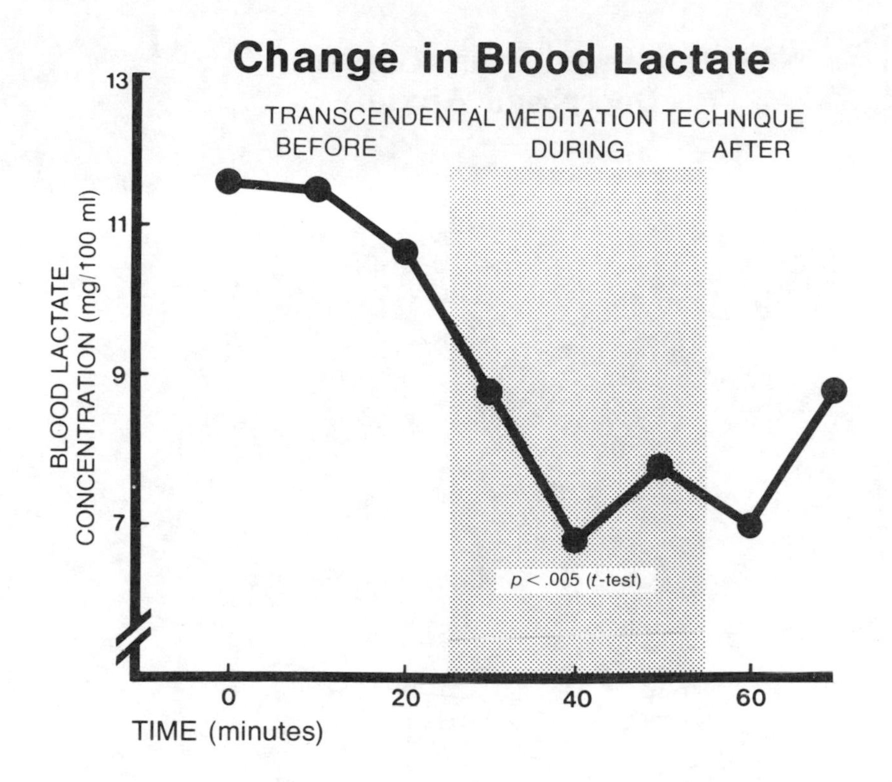

BIOCHEMISTRY OF DEEP REST

Finding: During the Transcendental Meditation technique the concentration of blood lactate markedly decreases and remains low some time after practice of the technique.

Interpretation: Decreased blood lactate is thought to indicate a profound state of muscular relaxation. A high concentration of lactate in the blood has been associated with anxiety neurosis, anxiety attacks, and high blood pressure. Therefore, the persistent decrease in lactate during and after the Transcendental Meditation technique is a biochemical correlate of an overall decrease in anxiety.

First Reference: Robert Keith Wallace and Herbert Benson, "The Physiology of Meditation," *Scientific American* 226, no. 2 (U.S.A.: 1972): 84–90.

Second Reference: Robert Keith Wallace, Herbert Benson, and Archie F. Wilson, "A Wakeful Hypometabolic Physiologic State," *American Journal of Physiology* 221, no. 3 (U.S.A.: 1971): 795–799.

As a result of the TM program, anxiety during activity is decreased.

Increased Inner Control, Decreased Anxiety

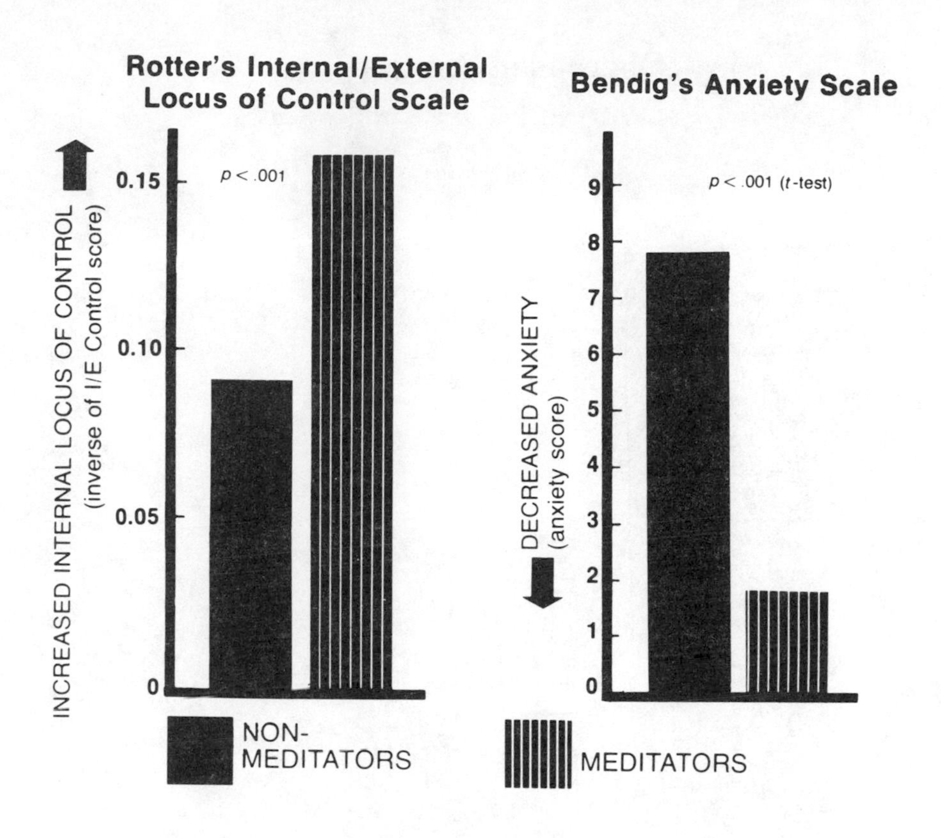

INCREASED INNER CONTROL
DECREASED ANXIETY

Finding: Compared with a control group of non-meditators, subjects practicing the Transcendental Meditation technique demonstrated a more internal locus of control, as measured by Rotter's Internal/External (IE) Locus of Control Scale, and were less anxious, as measured by Bendig's Anxiety Scale.

Interpretation: Internal control as measured by Rotter's scale indicates the development of broader comprehension — insight into the causal connection between one's behavior and the environment and foresight into the consequences of one's behavior. High internal locus of control has been associated with psychological adaptability, low anxiety, and the ability to effectively extract and make use of information from a complex environment. Since the TM technique stabilizes the internal sense of self and improves the integration and thereby the effectiveness of thought and action, the meditator naturally feels a greater sense of control over his life.

Reference: Larry A. Hjelle, "Transcendental Meditation and Psychological Health," *Perceptual and Motor Skills* 39 (U.S.A: 1974): 623-628.

Decreased Anxiety

Institute for Personality and Ability Testing Anxiety Scale

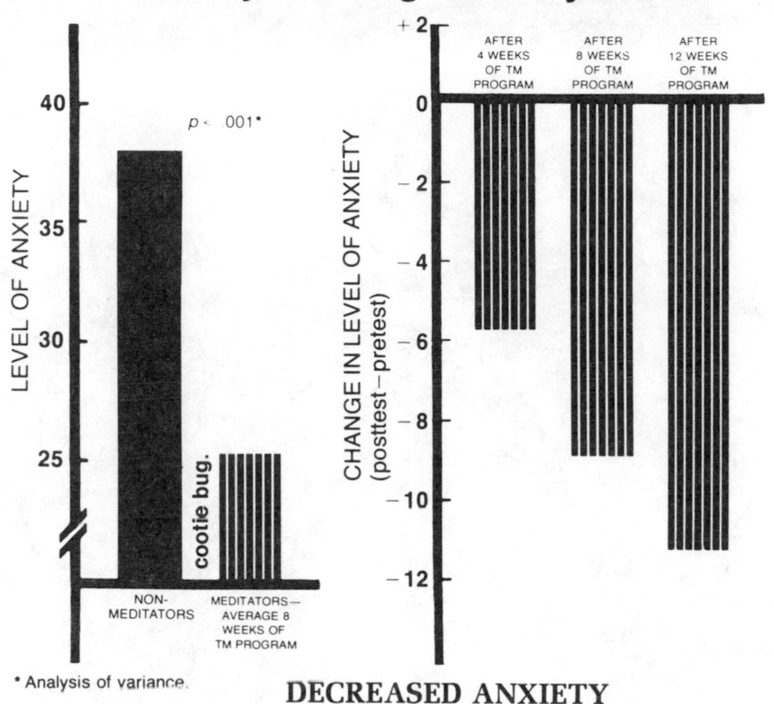

DECREASED ANXIETY

Finding: Research using the Institute for Personality and Ability Testing (IPAT) Anxiety Scale indicated that after beginning the Transcendental Meditation technique subjects showed a significant ($p. < .001$) decrease in anxiety level and exhibited significantly less anxiety than non-meditators. The reduction of anxiety was progressively greater with length of practice of the TM technique.

Interpretation: The Transcendental Meditation program produces a cumulative decrease in anxiety. Anxiety is associated with impairment of functioning in almost all areas of life — physiological, perceptual-motor, intellectual, and emotional. Anxiety also causes psychological rigidity and blockage of creativity. Therefore, a reduction in anxiety can be expected to be accompanied by greater availability of the individual's inherent resources in every area of life.

Reference: Zoe Lazar, Lawrence Farwell, and John T. Farrow, "The Effects of the Transcendental Meditation Program on Anxiety, Drug Abuse, Cigarette Smoking, and Alcohol Consumption," (Harvard University, Boston, Massachusetts, U.S.A.).

So our thoughts and feelings are more clearly and freely expressed.

Some other concrete improvements to health as a result of the TM program are:

Relief from Insomnia

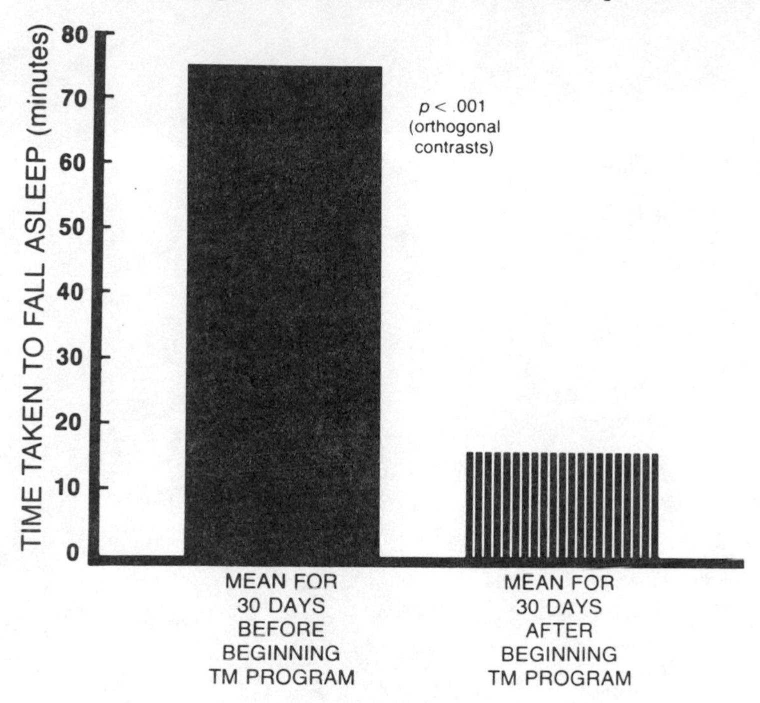

RELIEF FROM INSOMNIA

Finding: The Transcendental Meditation technique significantly reduced the time taken for insomniacs to fall asleep. As a therapy against insomnia, the Transcendental Meditation program was reported to be simple to administer, immediately effective, stable over time, and without unfavorable side effects.

Interpretation: The Transcendental Meditation technique relieves deep-seated stress from the nervous system on a direct physiological level. Consequently, it produces a wide range of beneficial effects without requiring specific attention to any one area. The effect seen here — greater regularity in the sleeping cycle — was subsequently shown to be stable throughout the first year of practice of the TM technique and can therefore not be accounted for by a placebo effect (see second reference). The results of this study reflect a stabilization of basic biological rhythms, one aspect of a holistic stabilization of daily life.

First Reference: Donald E. Miskiman, "The Treatment of Insomnia by the Transcendental Meditation Technique," (University of Alberta, Edmonton, Alberta, Canada).

Second Reference: Donald E. Miskiman, "Long-Term Effects of the Transcendental Meditation Technique on the Treatment of Insomnia," (University of Alberta, Edmonton, Alberta, Canada).

Even though the body may be very tired quite often tension interferes with sleep. The TM technique practiced for 15–20 minutes in the morning and again before supper removes tension so that the body can function in the most efficient and natural way. Because it removes tension, the TM technique helps us get a good night's sleep.

Beneficial Effects on Bronchial Asthma

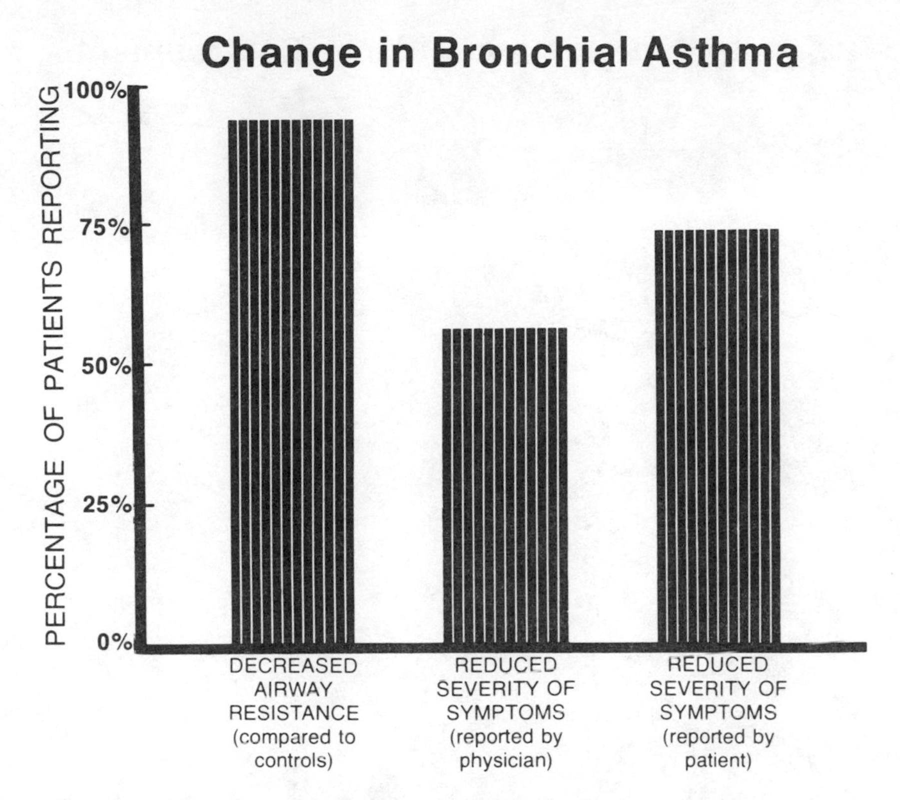

BENEFICIAL EFFECTS ON BRONCHIAL ASTHMA

Finding: After beginning the practice of the Transcendental Meditation technique 94 percent of a group of asthmatic patients showed improvement as determined by the physiological measurement of airway resistance. Fifty-five percent of the asthmatic patients showed improvement as reported by their personal physicians, and 74 percent showed improvement as reported by the patients themselves.

Interpretation: These results indicate that the Transcendental Meditation program is beneficial for patients with bronchial asthma. Bronchial asthma is one of a group of diseases the severity of which has been consistently correlated with the level of psychological stress of the individual. By systematically relieving stress, the Transcendental Meditation program promises to be an effective new adjunct to therapy for this and other psychosomatic diseases.

First Reference: Ron Honsberger and Archie F. Wilson, "The Effect of Transcendental Meditation upon Bronchial Asthma," *Clinical Research* 22, no. 2 (U.S.A.: 1973)

Second Reference: Ron Honsberger and Archie F. Wilson, "Transcendental Meditation in Treating Asthma," *Respiratory Therapy: The Journal of Inhalation Technology* 3, no. 6 (U.S.A.: 1973): 79–80.

Third Reference: Archie F. Wilson, Ron Honsberger, J.T. Chiu, and H.S. Novey, "Transcendental Meditation and Asthma," *Respiration* 32 (U.S.A.: 1973): 74–80.

Fourth Reference: Paul W. Corey, "Airway Conductance and Oxygen Consumption Changes Associated with Practice of the Transcendental Meditation Technique," (University of Colorado Medical Center, Denver, Colorado, U.S.A.).

What about new stresses?

A stronger nervous system doesn't acquire stress so easily.

Effective Interaction with the Environment

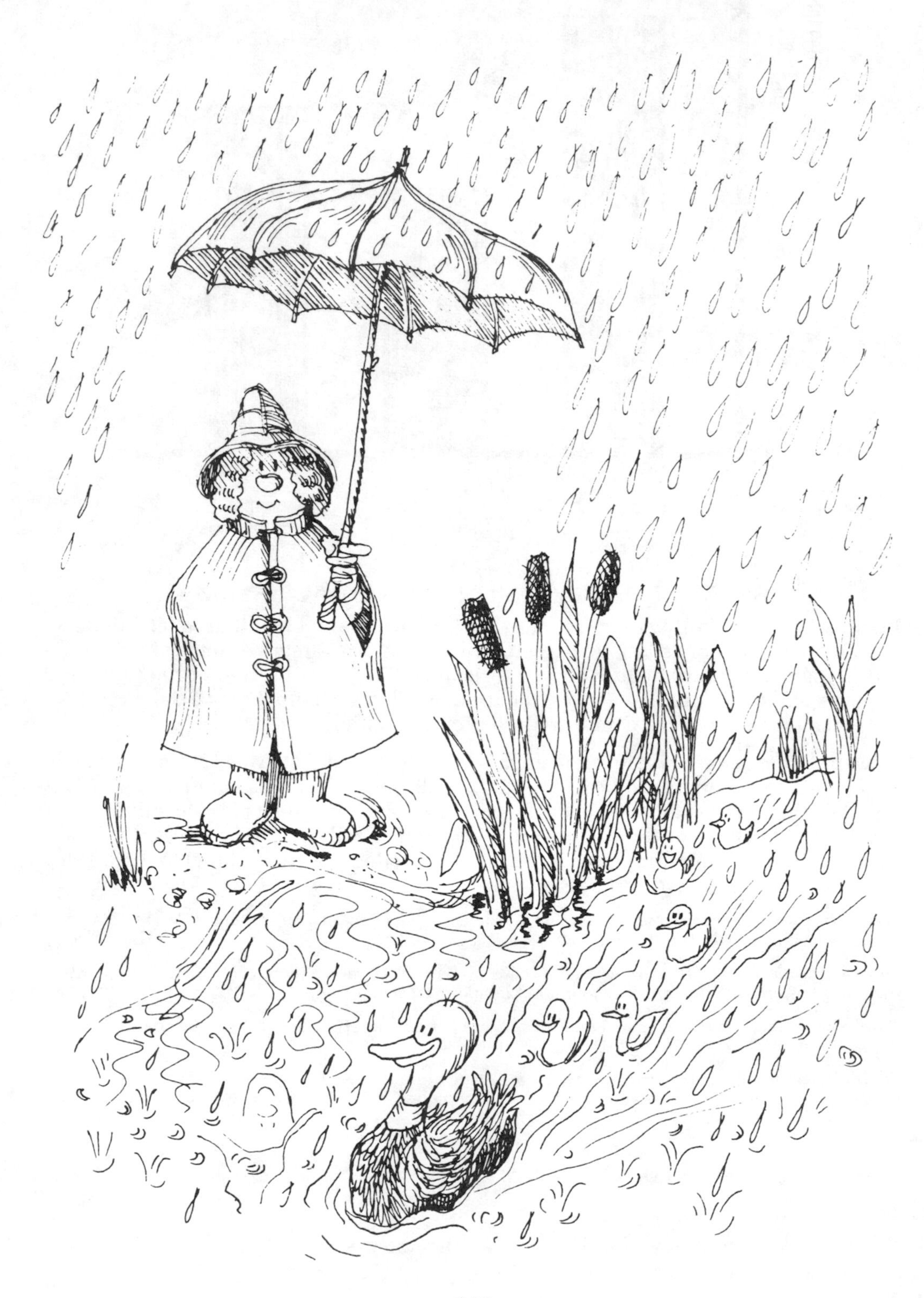

Habituation of Skin Resistance Responses

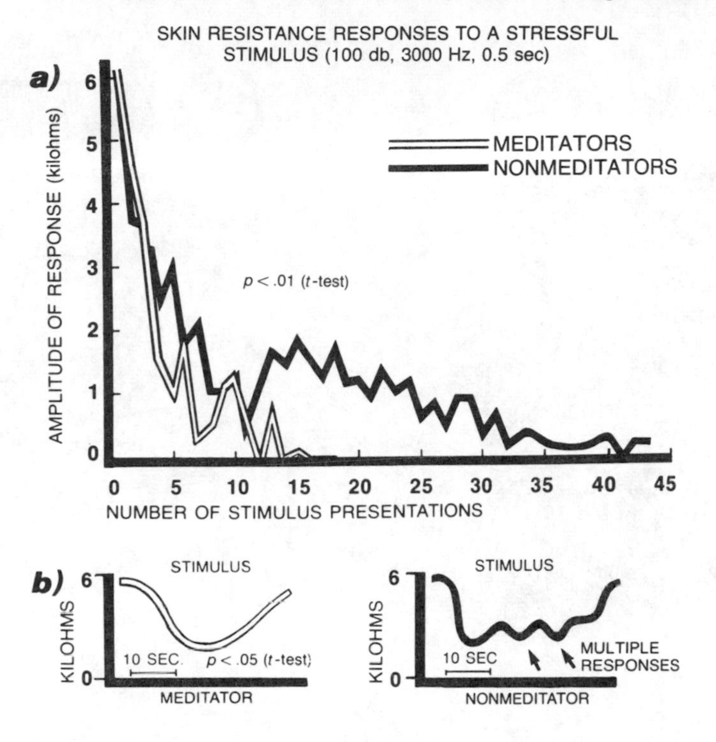

EFFECTIVE INTERACTION WITH THE ENVIRONMENT

Finding: In this study induced changes in skin resistance in response to a stressful stimulus were measured. Both the wave form of the individual response and the degree of habituation (reduced response) to repeated stimuli were recorded. Subjects practicing the Transcendental Meditation technique were found to habituate more rapidly to a series of auditory stresses (loud noises) than non-meditators (figure *a*). In addition, the wave form of the response to the first stress was significantly smoother and more stable in the meditators (figure *b*).

Interpretation: Those practicing the TM technique recover from stress more quickly than non-meditators. This faster habituation is known from other psychophysiological studies to be correlated with a more mature style of functioning of the nervous system and a more stable and expressive personality. In addition, meditators show a smoother style of response to stressful stimuli than non-meditators, indicating a more stable functioning of the nervous system in general. The practice of the Transcendental Meditation technique strengthens the individual's nervous system and allows him to function more effectively in a stressful environment.

Reference: David W. Orme-Johnson, "Autonomic Stability and Transcendental Meditation," *Psychosomatic Medicine* 35, no. 4 (U.S.A.: 1973): 341–349.

Faster Recovery from Sleep Deprivation

Response to Sleep Deprivation

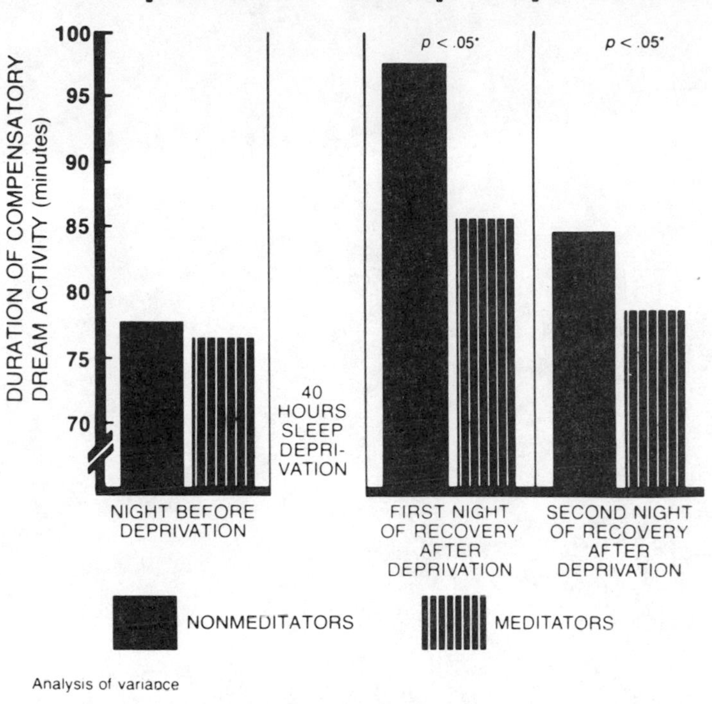

FASTER RECOVERY FROM SLEEP DEPRIVATION

Finding: Measurements showed that after 40 hours of sleep deprivation a group of subjects practicing the Transcendental Meditation technique recovered much more quickly than a control group of nonmeditators. Recovery was measured by duration of compensatory dreaming.

Interpretation: Sleep deprivation is a highly stressful experience, and compensatory dreaming is thought to be a form of stress release. The meditator's nervous system becomes more resilient and less subject to long-term disruption by a stressful experience. Faster recovery after exposure to stress of this type is valuable not only to people in everyday life but also to those in critical occupations, such as military, police, airline, and hospital personnel. This study also suggests that the TM technique may be helpful in the problem of jet lag.

Reference: Donald E. Miskiman, "The Effect of the Transcendental Meditation Technique on Compensatory Paradoxical Sleep," (University of Alberta, Edmonton, Alberta, Canada).

Something that is stressful when we're weak or tired can be dealt with easily when we're strong and alert. TM'ers recover more quickly from stressful situations.

This is because of the growth of stability and adaptability with TM.

But I'm enjoying life already! Why should I practice the TM program?

The TM program produces rapid growth, expansion, evolution, increased intelligence, energy, creativity, happiness. It is not necessary to have a *deficiency* in any of these values to enjoy having more. No matter how energetic, intelligent, and creative we are, we enjoy life when we become *more* energetic, intelligent, and creative.

This is Growth—a Fundamental of Progress.

GROWTH

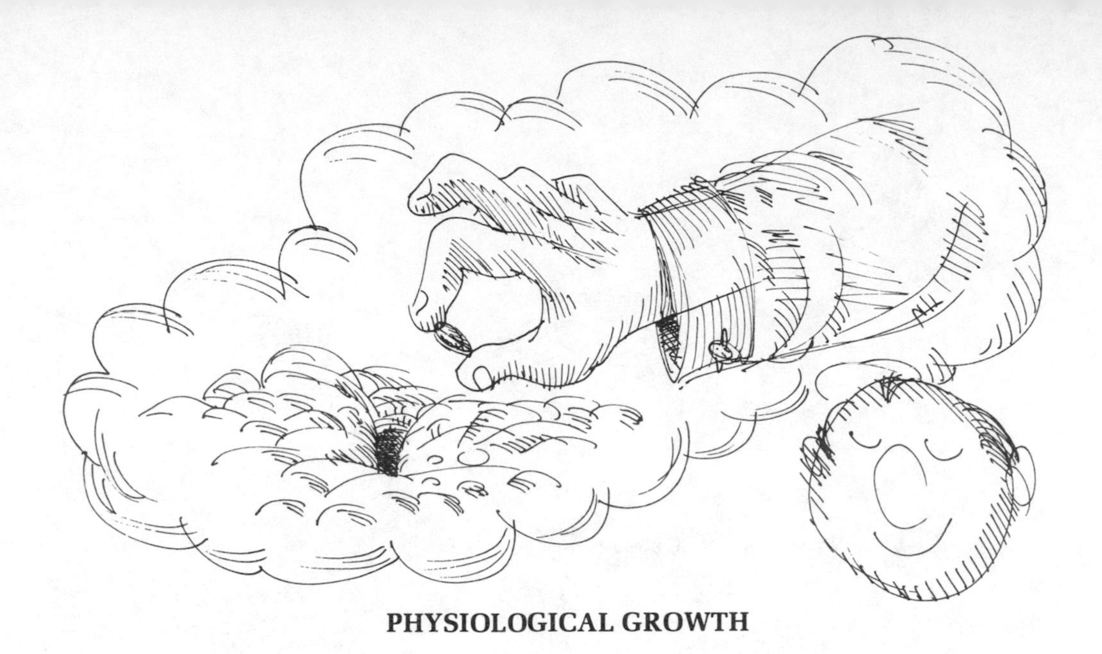

PHYSIOLOGICAL GROWTH

Through the practice of the TRANSCENDENTAL MEDITATION technique, physiological growth—more efficient and effective physiological functioning—increases, as indicated by:

growing strength and orderliness of brain functioning

growing cardiovascular efficiency

growing respiratory efficiency

growing resistance to disease

growing refinement of perception

growing stability of the autonomic nervous system

growing neuromuscular efficiency

growing effectiveness in sports

growing physiological adaptability, stability, integration, and purification

The metabolic rate decreases more during the TRANSCENDENTAL MEDITATION technique than during sleep, yet the brain wave patterns during meditation indicate a state of alertness rather than the dullness of sleep. The addition of this unique state of restful alertness to one's daily routine of rest and activity has been found to promote the growth of a superior quality of physiological functioning.

It is our daily experience that rest is the procedure for increasing physiological efficiency and effectiveness. Inefficient functioning of the physical system during the waking state, experienced as fatigue and dullness, is transformed through the mechanics of the sleep state into efficient physiological functioning, experienced as liveliness and clarity of the mind. This day-by-day rejuvenation of the system supports growing physiological efficiency.

The TRANSCENDENTAL MEDITATION technique works by the same natural principle, increasing physiological efficiency through rest. Because the TRANSCENDENTAL MEDITATION technique produces an even deeper rest than sleep, it is not surprising that the growth of physiological efficiency and effectiveness is greatly enhanced in meditators.

These physiological changes account for the psychological changes.

PSYCHOLOGICAL GROWTH

Through the practice of the TRANSCENDENTAL MEDITATION technique, psychological growth—the development of full potential of thinking, understanding, and feeling—is enhanced and enriched, as indicated by:

- growing creativity
- growing intelligence
- growing efficiency and staying power
- growing academic performance
- growing learning ability
- growing orderliness of thinking
- growing spontaneity and capacity for intimate contact
- growing self-actualization
- growing self-esteem
- growing inner control
- growing sociability and friendliness
- growing emotional stability and self-sufficiency
- growing innovation
- growing tolerance
- growing individuality

This holistic value of psychological growth involving the simultaneous development of the abilities of thinking, understanding, and feeling is called evolution of consciousness. Growth is restricted when the process of growth starts to offer stress. Relative growth alone, untouched by the field of the Absolute, provides no opportunity for the full expression of creative intelligence. This makes it obvious that the growth of awareness of the absolute phase of life is vital, for the relative growth is so insane that it stops its own path. It is made sane by the growth of consciousness, and then it ceases to generate resistance on its own path; instead, it accelerates its speed and arrives at the goal quickly—the goal of fulfillment, the resultant value of the evolution of consciousness.

These physiological and psychological changes account for the sociological changes.

SOCIOLOGICAL GROWTH

Through the practice of the TRANSCENDENTAL MEDITATION technique, sociological growth—the growth of harmony in society—is accelerated and enriched, as indicated by:

- growing sociability
- improving interpersonal relationships
- growing productivity and improving performance in organizations
- growing job satisfaction
- growing social adequacy
- growing naturalness and outgoingness
- growing effectiveness of rehabilitation
- improved quality of life

The potential for the growth of individual consciousness is enormous and, on the basis of developed individual awareness through the TRANSCENDENTAL MEDITATION program, the growth of achievement and fulfillment possible in society is virtually unlimited. The achievements of society leading up to modern times are impressive even though psychologists have agreed that only a fraction of human potential is being utilized. When full human potential is developed through the implementation of Maharishi's World Plan, the world will enjoy an age of unprecedented brilliance—generation after generation.

These physiological, psychological, and sociological changes account for the ecological changes.

ECOLOGICAL GROWTH

Ecological growth is the expression of growing wholeness of life. For man this ecological wholeness has its value in:

the development of wholeness of life within himself:

self-actualization

the development of the ability to appreciate wholeness in his environment:

broadened awareness, increased perceptual ability, and increased learning ability

the development of the ability to refrain from disrupting regulatory mechanisms responsible for the preservation of ecological stability and growth:

increased intelligence, respect, and self-sufficiency

the development of the ability to project and promote life-supporting influences to enrich and strengthen those fundamental mechanisms in nature responsible for all ecological stability and growth:

increased liveliness, naturalness, spontaneity, innovation, energy, creativity, good humor, and cordiality

This is how man, the most influential member of the ecosphere, contributes maximum effect to ecological growth through his daily practice of the TRANSCENDENTAL MEDITATION technique. Ecological growth—the expression of wholeness of life in man and in nature—constitutes the supreme state of all growth. This supreme state of growth has traditionally been known as spiritual value.

The TM technique improves perception, for example. We all enjoy perceiving more clearly. I'm sure you've noticed that some days, when you're rested and fresh, the world seems alive! A beautiful place! Music seems more enchanting, a friend more delightful. This is just improved perception. Everyone wants that.

Couldn't that improved perception be overwhelming?

The TM program develops *all* aspects of human ability, spontaneously, in a balanced, integrated way. So we'll never find one quality developing at the expense of any other. To balance perception the TM program develops attention—the increased ability to focus.

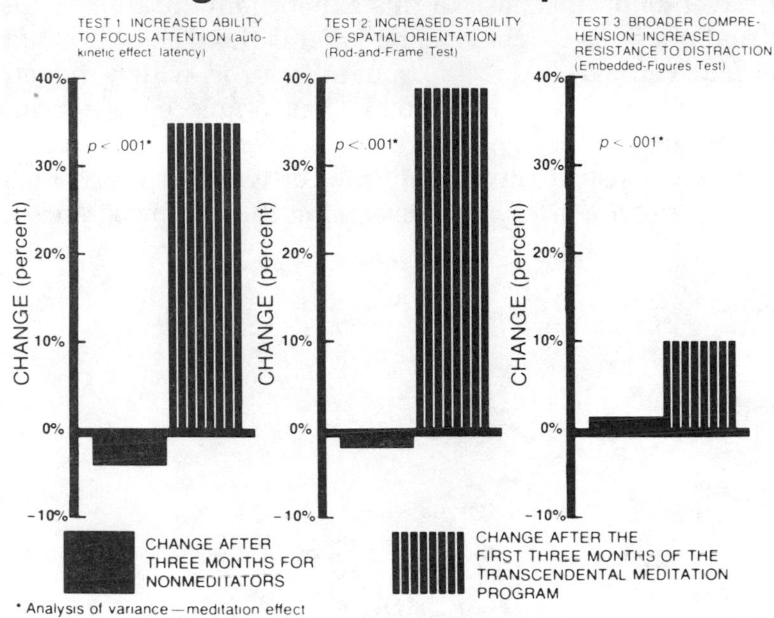

BROADER COMPREHENSION AND IMPROVED ABILITY TO FOCUS ATTENTION

Finding: In this study three tests were administered that directly measure field independence, the ability to focus attention on specific objects without being distracted by the environment of the objects. Meditators changed significantly in the direction of increased field independence after practicing the Transcendental Meditation technique for three months, compared with a non-meditating control group.

The latency of the autokinetic effect measures the time it takes a subject to perceive movement of a spot of light; the Rod-and-Frame Test measures the ability to orient a rod to true vertical position against a tilted frame; and the Embedded-Figures Test measures the ability to perceive simple figures embedded in a complex background.

Interpretation: These measures indicate the development of field independence, the ability to analytically perceive an item embedded in a complex context. Researchers have found that persons with greater field independence have the following characteristics: greater ability to assimilate and structure experience; greater organization of mind and cognitive clarity; improved memory; greater creative expression; stable internal frame of reference; stable standards, attitudes, judgement, and sentiments without continuous reference to external standards; differentiation of inner and outer; autonomic stability; more assertiveness. All these characteristics are indications of improved neurological organization and, consequently, more evolved consciousness. This improvement in meditators is all the more remarkable because it was previously believed that these basic perceptual abilities do not improve beyond early adulthood.

First Reference: Kenneth R. Pelletier, "The Effects of the Transcendental Meditation Program on Perceptual Style: Increased Field Independence," (University of California School of Medicine, San Francisco, California, U.S.A.).

Second Reference: Kenneth R. Pelletier, "Influence of Transcendental Meditation upon Autokinetic Perception," *Perceptual and Motor Skills 39* (U.S.A.: 1974): 1031–1034.

One feature of this chart is particularly interesting—the Rod and Frame test in the middle section of the chart. In this experiment the subject sits in a dark room. In front of him is a lighted square that is tilted so it does not represent horizontal and vertical. Inside the square is a rod which the subject must adjust to true vertical. This means that he has to ignore his impression of the tilted environment, the lighted frame, and depend on his own inner perceptions—his sense of gravity and true vertical. The graph illustrates that the subjects scored much higher after taking the TM program.

So what does this really show?

It shows that even though perception does become increasingly refined, inner stability and discrimination are also improved. Psychologists call this "field independence"; that is, the subject acts from his own information and inner awareness, and thus he can successfully disregard irrelevant or distracting information from his environment, or "field."

Other research has established that people who are field-independent are active, independent, not submissive, and less anxious. They have fewer spontaneous galvanic skin responses (see page 103), more self-esteem, and more favorable beliefs about human nature.

Psychologists call such people "self-actualized." This means that their own inner nature, or inner potential, is actualized, made real. TM'ers grown in self-actualization.

Increased Self-Actualization

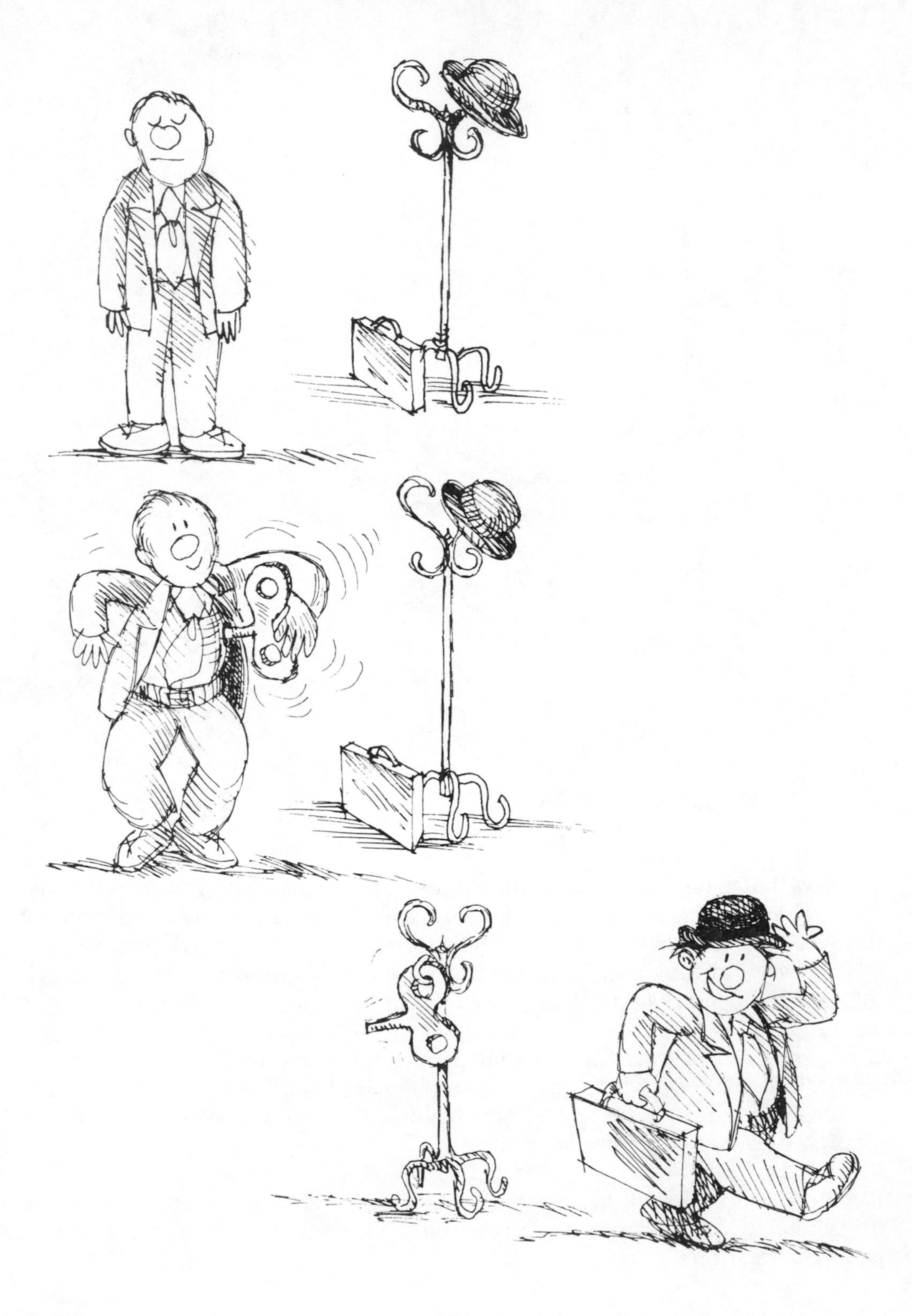

Northridge Developmental Scale

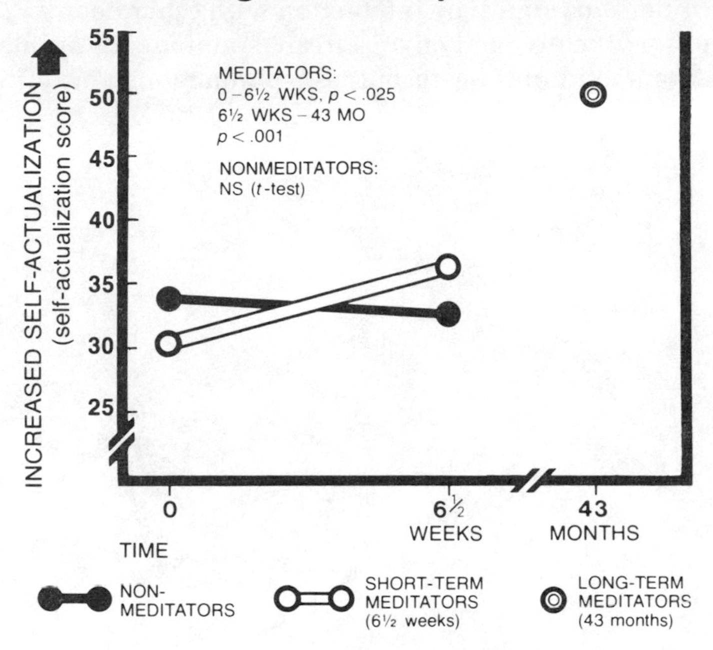

INCREASED SELF-ACTUALIZATION

Finding: Subjects practicing the Transcendental Meditation technique for an average of 1.5 months showed a significant increase in self-actualization compared with a group of non-meditators, as measured by the Northridge Developmental Scale. The level of self-actualization was highest in long-term (average 43 months) meditators (as denoted by the double circle on the chart), indicating that the benefits of the Transcendental Meditation program are cumulative.

Interpretation: Growth of self-actualization as defined by this test includes the development of the following qualities: open, receptive, caring attitude; cheerfulness and good humor; predominance of positive thinking; spontaneity and freshness of appreciation; self-sufficiency; loss of fear of death; affective readiness for developing consciousness; discovery of opportunities for creativity; acceptance of self, nature, and others; conscious sense of destiny. This study shows that the Transcendental Meditation programme allows the personality to unfold naturally in the direction of self-actualization on the basis of an increasingly refined nervous system.

Reference: Phillip C. Ferguson and John C. Gowan. "Psychological Findings on Transcendental Meditation," (Paper presented to the California State Psychological Association, Fresno, California. U.S.A., 1974), *Journal of Humanistic Psychology* (in press).

Self-actualized people are inner-directed; they're motivated from within. They enjoy solitude, and they enjoy interaction with other people. They have superior perception of reality and enjoy a fresh, spontaneous appreciation of life. They're in command of their resources, spontaneous and fulfilled.

Whew! All those benefits!

Fortunately the TM program integrates all these changes into one's life in a natural and balanced way. This brings us to our last Fundamental of Progress, Integration.

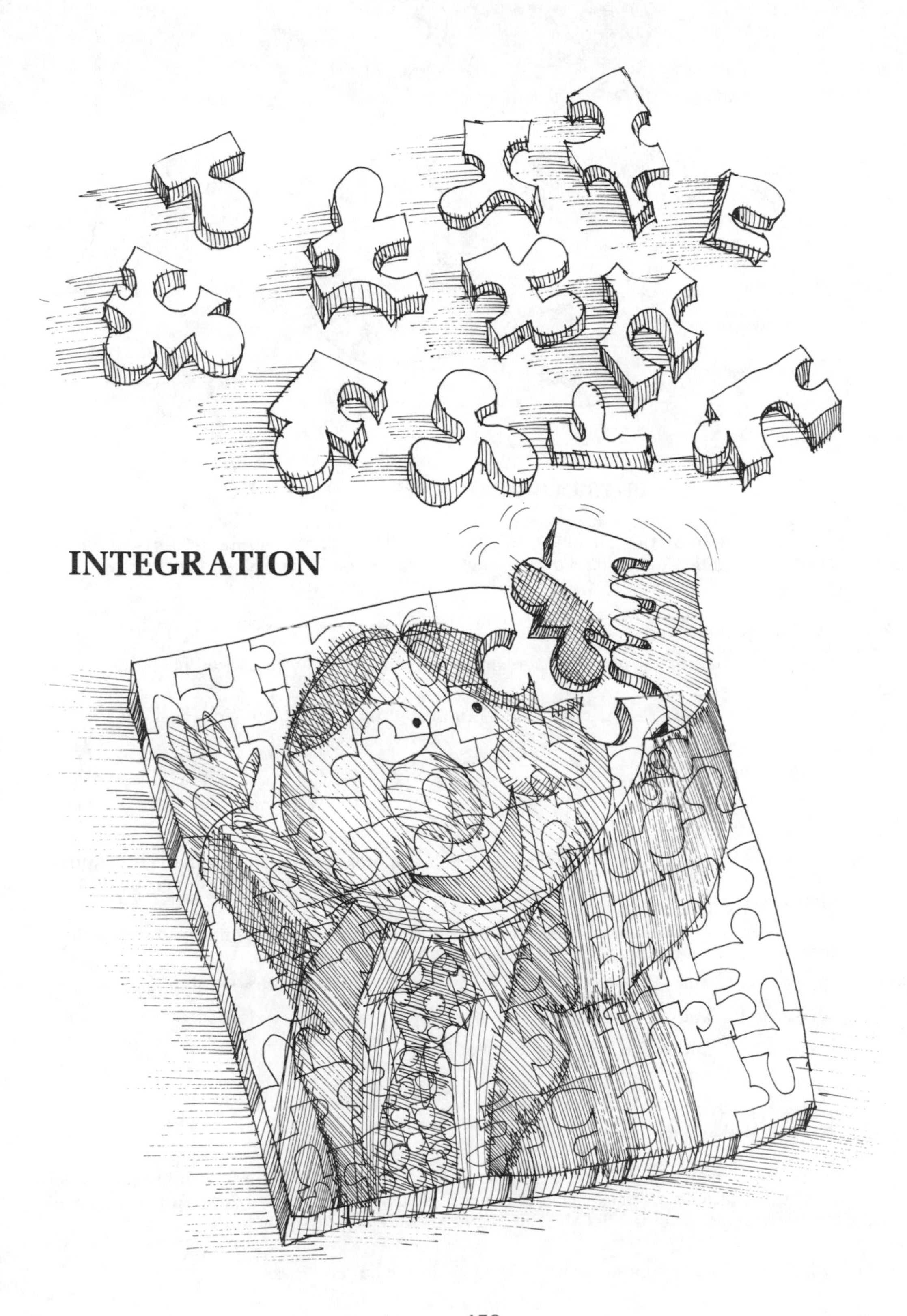

INTEGRATION

PHYSIOLOGICAL INTEGRATION

Through the practice of the TRANSCENDENTAL MEDITATION technique, physiological integration—integration of the physical system and its smooth coordinated functioning—increases, as indicated by:

- neuromuscular integration
- integrated functioning of the sensory apparatus, indicated by improved perception and attention
- integrated state of "restful alertness" as indicated by simultaneous changes in:
  - metabolic rate
  - biochemistry
  - electrophysiology
  - electroencephalography
- integrated functioning of the left and right hemispheres of the brain, implying functional integration of the analytic and verbal skills of the left hemisphere with the synthetic and spatial skills of the right hemisphere
- integrated functioning of the front and back of the brain, implying improved, integrated functioning of thinking and thought-action coordination
- increased stability, harmony, balance, and coherence of brain functioning
- increased integration of the immune system resulting in improved resistance to disease
- integration of mind and body as indicated by:
  - faster reactions
  - superior perceptual-motor performance
  - improved athletic performance

The observations mentioned above, with reference to coordinated brain functioning, suggest increasing integration of both aspects of the brain waves—their structure and function—total integration resulting from the TRANSCENDENTAL MEDITATION technique.

These physiological changes account for the psychological changes.

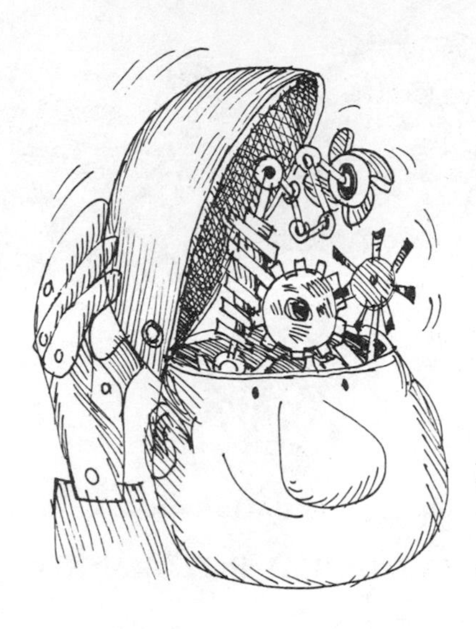

PSYCHOLOGICAL INTEGRATION

Through the practice of the TRANSCENDENTAL MEDITATION technique, psychological integration—the integration of all faculties of the mind: thinking, understanding, and feeling—increases, as indicated by:

- increased integration of intellect:
  - increased intelligence
  - increased learning ability
  - improved academic performance
  - increased orderliness of thinking
  - improved discriminative capacity
- increased integration of heart and mind
- increased integration of action:
  - increased creativity
  - increased innovation
  - increased energy level
  - increased efficiency
  - increased productivity
  - increased perceptual-motor performance
  - faster reactions
  - improved athletic performance
- increased integration of personality:
  - increased self-actualization
  - increased naturalness and spontaneity
  - increased wholeness and unity of person
  - increased individuality

All faculties of the mind—thinking, feeling, and understanding—have a common basis in pure consciousness. For profound integration, it is necessary to take the mind towards this unifying field of consciousness.

Applying this phenomenon of integration of the mind to the practicalities of business, industry, and progress, what we find is that although productivity and progress necessitate both routine work and a broad basis of comprehension, the paradox of productivity is that the act of habitually focusing the mind during routine work keeps awareness within narrow boundaries, restricting broad comprehension. This restriction to the full expression of creative intelligence makes life uncomfortable and remains as a seed for frustration and discontent, which expresses itself in various modes of suffering and negativity in life. The experience of unbounded awareness during the TRANSCENDENTAL MEDITATION technique counterbalances the narrowing influence of routine work on the mind. In this way, one can maintain the benefit of routine work and eliminate the restricting influence on broad comprehension.

These physiological and psychological changes account for the sociological changes.

SOCIOLOGICAL INTEGRATION

Through the practice of the TRANSCENDENTAL MEDITATION technique, sociological integration—the harmonious coexistence, coordinated growth, and mutual fulfillment of the different behavioral patterns of society—increases, as indicated by:

more rewarding and productive interpersonal relationships among executives and employees

increased integrating influences:

- more respect
- increased cordiality
- increased tolerance
- increased contentment
- increased sociability
- increased naturalness and spontaneity

decreased discordant influences:

- decreased irritability
- decreased anxiety
- decreased social inadequacy

decreased stress and increased acceptable social behavior of prisoners

reduced use of alcohol, cigarettes, and nonprescribed drugs

decreased crime rate

Social disharmony and discord in the family of nations, on the basis of national boundaries made rigid on the level of awareness of the people, produce the same influence as grows through routine work. (Refer to Psychological Integration.) All international conflicts and wars throughout the ages and the continuing situation of wars and conflicts in every generation are, from this point of view, based on the nonavailability of unbounded awareness, which can counterbalance the rigidity caused by the importance laid on national boundaries to the exclusion of international significance. Now with the TRANSCENDENTAL MEDITATION technique, unbounded awareness is available to all; the national boundaries will enjoy the flavor of international significance, and their narrowing influence will be neutralized. Here is the expression of the supreme value of sociological integration, which the TRANSCENDENTAL MEDITATION program is capable of providing.

These physiological, psychological, and sociological changes account for the ecological changes.

ECOLOGICAL INTEGRATION

Through the practice of the TRANSCENDENTAL MEDITATION technique, ecological integration—the wholeness of the individual's relationship with his environment—blossoms, as a result of the total effect of the practice, which increases:

physiological integration

psychological integration

sociological integration

Air flowing over cool water takes the cold from the surface of the water and makes everything cool wherever it flows. The air flowing over hot water spreads the influence of heat all around. This explains the way in which the quality of the individual spreads in his environment. The TRANSCENDENTAL MEDITATION program, developing unbounded awareness, produces such a holistic value of integration in the individual that all fields of life—physiological, psychological, and sociological—are integrated simultaneously, and this produces a lively, concentrated, and powerful center of integration in the individual from where the influence of integration spontaneously radiates all around the whole of the environment and reverberates through the whole of the ecosphere. The process of ecological integration continues as the practice of the TRANSCENDENTAL MEDITATION technique continues—twice a day meditation, twice a day integration.

All this sounds very scientific, but I always thought meditation had something to do with "enlightenment."

There's nothing unscientific or mystical about enlightenment. Enlightenment simply means a state of mind and nervous system in which 100% of our potential is available for use. Another way to look at it is that enlightenment is the state of awareness produced by a nervous system with no stress and strain, a mind using full mental potential. Scientific research has shown that enlightenment is a very specific, permanent state of enjoyment. Consciousness is not restricted by structural or chemical imbalances in the system and can shine forth in its true value. This is all so different from our usual 5–15% efficiency that this beautiful state of life has become legend. Now, thanks to the TM program, it is available for everyone to enjoy.

But I thought to gain enlightenment you had to give away all your possessions, perform rigid disciplines and live in a cave for the rest of your life.

The severity of that life style doesn't sound very enticing, does it? This misunderstanding of the road to enlightenment is why for thousands of years people with responsibilities in society have thought enlightenment to be difficult and impractical—something for monks and recluses, requiring fantastic will power.

We in this generation are deeply indebted to Maharishi and to his teacher, Guru Dev, for providing an effortless, extremely rapid technique for everyone to achieve this most practical and basic of human goals.

This one of Maharishi's main points, that enlightenment—using one's full potential—is *everyone's* birthright and that it can be easily attained by us all.

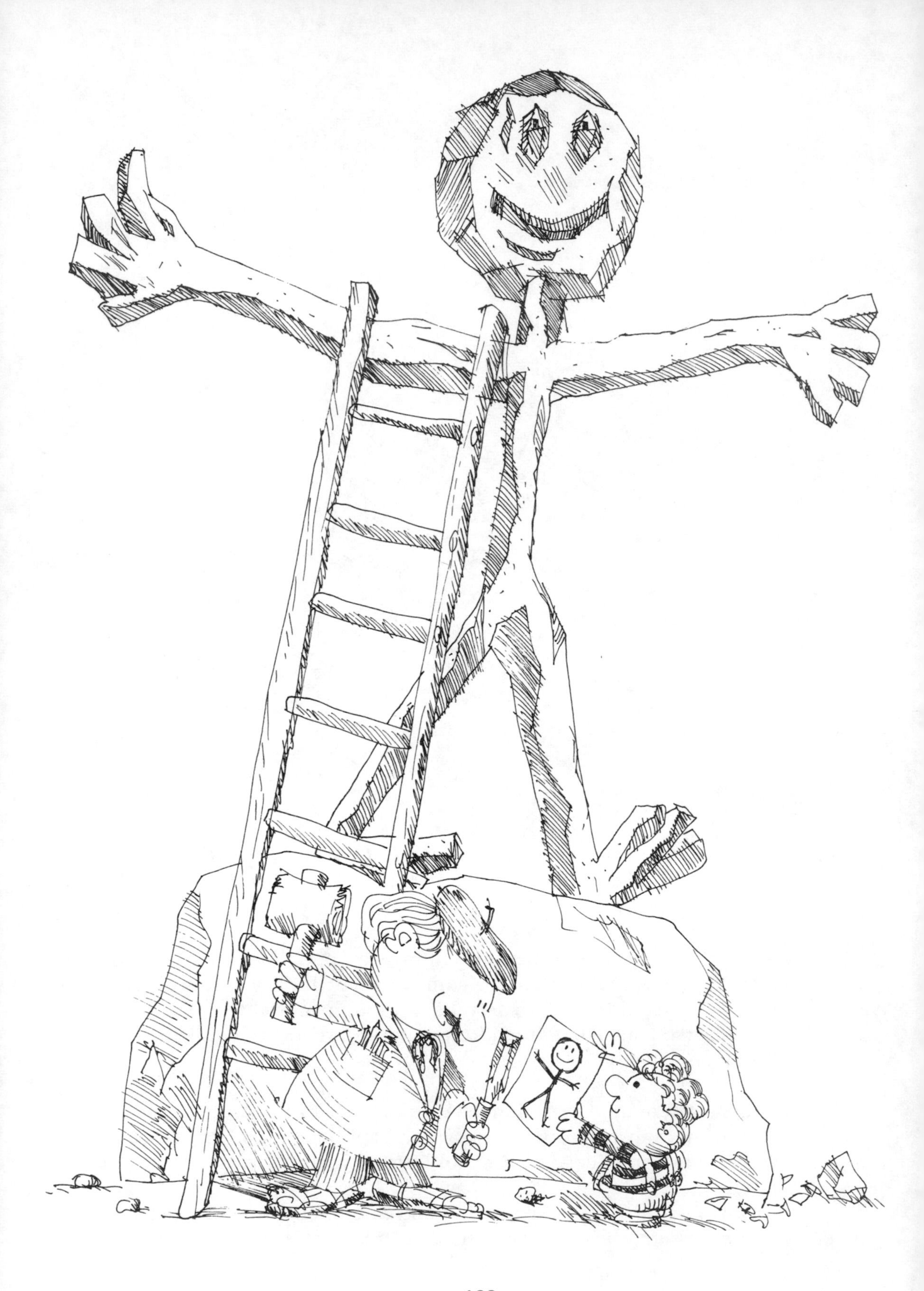

How does the TM program make one more creative?

The TM technique increases our contact with the source of creativity within us. Also, it removes stress from the nervous system, making us more sensitive and more responsive to our environment. Greater intelligence, perception, and clarity of mind automatically bring expanded creativity.

A common misconception about creativity is that it is limited to the rather narrow field of "the arts." Creativity is a daily experience—an exciting way of dealing with all the situations of living. To create is to feel alive.

Another misconception is that creativity depends on suffering or tension. Actually, tension inhibits creativity, just as it interferes with every other area of life. The more sensitive, responsive, stable, and intelligent we are, the more creative we will be. The more we perceive and understand, the more we can express and share.

Increased Creativity

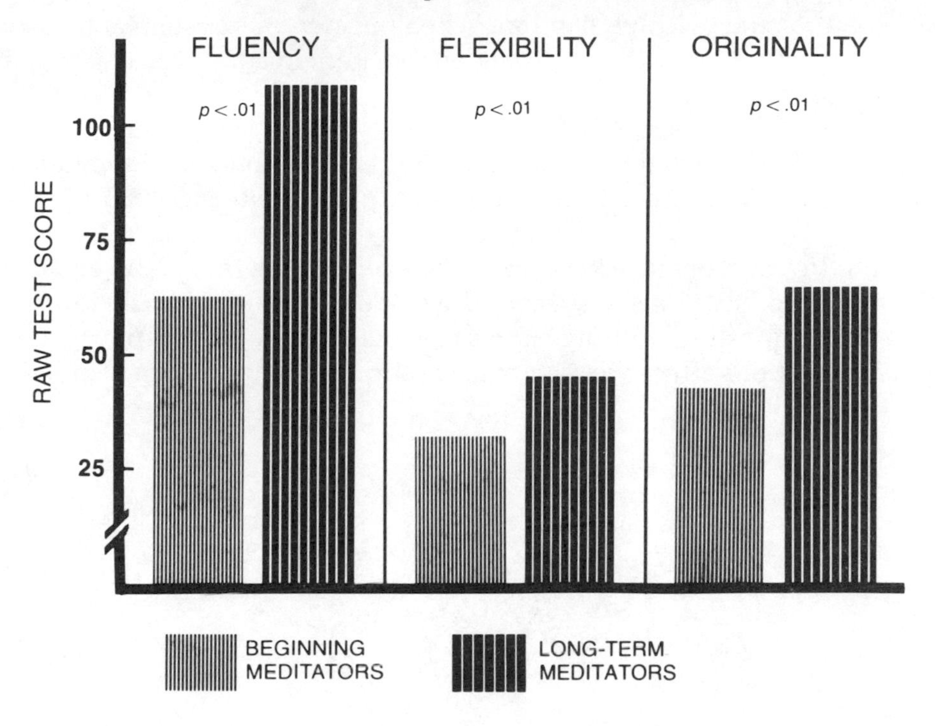

INCREASED CREATIVITY

Finding: The Torrance Test of Creative Thinking (TTCT), Verbal Form A, was used to compare 44 subjects practicing the Transcendental Meditation technique for an average of 18 months with 41 subjects who had just learned the Transcendental Meditation technique. The two groups were equivalent in age, sex, education, and income level. The long-term meditators scored significantly higher ($p<.01$) on all three scales of the TTCT—Fluency, Flexibility, and Originality—indicating that practice of the Transcendental Meditation technique increases creativity.

Interpretation: The TTCT was developed to measure the type of creative thinking process described by eminent scientific researchers, inventors, and creative writers. Psychologists such as Carl Rogers and Abraham Maslow have associated this type of creativity with increased self-actualization, which has also been found by independent studies to result from the Transcendental Meditation program. These findings give objective validation to the statement that the Transcendental Meditation program systematically develops creative intelligence by providing a means to directly experience the source of creativity in the mind. The aspects of creativity measured here—fluency, flexibility, and originality—may be associated with integration, adaptability, and growth, three of the fundamentals of progress that are enhanced by the Transcendental Meditation technique.

Reference: Michael J. MacCallum, "The Transcendental Meditation Program and Creativity" (California State University, Long Beach, California, U.S.A.).

Does this creativity extend to my personal relationships?

Absolutely. It begins with perception. When our nervous system is free from stress and our mind is clear and expanded, we perceive the world as a joyful place. We appreciate life more.

This appreciation grows until it can only be referred to as love. Love is the automatic, ultimate appreciation of a person, place, or thing.

We send out love; we get love in return. "For every action there is an equal and opposite reaction." We love, we receive love. We hate, and find hate returned. This is simple physics. Nothing in the universe exists in isolation. All our thoughts and actions affect every atom in creation, and every atom responds in kind.

So we should try to love.

No. There should be no trying involved. Loving is the natural state of man. Man was not born for suffering. Man was born to enjoy life, to radiate this enjoyment for all to share. This is the natural, spontaneous experience of evolution: greater joy and happiness, and increased expression of this fulfillment.

It is this natural tendency to radiate goodness when we are feeling happy that is the basis of the social benefits of the Transcendental Meditation program. Like a current running through a filament, when joy enlivens the human nervous system, the system has no choice but to express this joy, this understanding, this appreciation of life.

spontaneous

And this joy comes from——

The expanded potential of the mind and the increased clarity of the nervous system. Radiation of warmth, love, happiness is the natural result of joy. There is no "mood making" here.

"Mood making"?

When you try to love, what you're doing is "trying," not loving. You create a "mood" of loving. In return, you receive a "mood," not love. Have you ever visited an office in which no one really likes anyone else, and everyone knows no one likes anyone, yet everyone smiles and pretends to be loving just the same?

No one is fooled by artificial warmth, not really.

Another danger of "mood making" is a loss of reality—life becomes a game that seems to have no end. Now we have a simple technique that makes individuals individual, makes the enjoyment of life genuine, makes relationships real.

With the TM technique the nervous system is spontaneously relieved of stress, the mind automatically expanded. This leads to natural appreciation, which grows to effortless loving. You will notice there is no trying involved in this entire process. From the technique through the inevitable sharing of love, every step is effortless, natural, spontaneous.

The growth of awareness and sensitivity, using the TM technique, is systematic. Our emotions do not become "mechanized," but the process that spontaneously leads to more and more loving is scientific and predictable.

Are we still capable of maintaining one-to-one intimate relationships?

Still capable? *Finally* capable!

All relationships are enhanced and warmed if one or more of the individuals is practicing the TM program. It's only logical: people who are sensitive, aware, lively, and warm are a joy to be around. On days when you're feeling good, it's easy to be with your friends. It's easy to love. It flows naturally. As we follow the TM program, we feel good more and more often. We draw the best people to us, and draw the best from those people.

All the limitations we once felt in our intimate relationships—anger, jealousy, insecurity, fear, depression—significantly decrease. We become understanding, patient, tender—truly loving. And we don't have to try for it—it's automatic.

Development of Personality

Personal Orientation Inventory

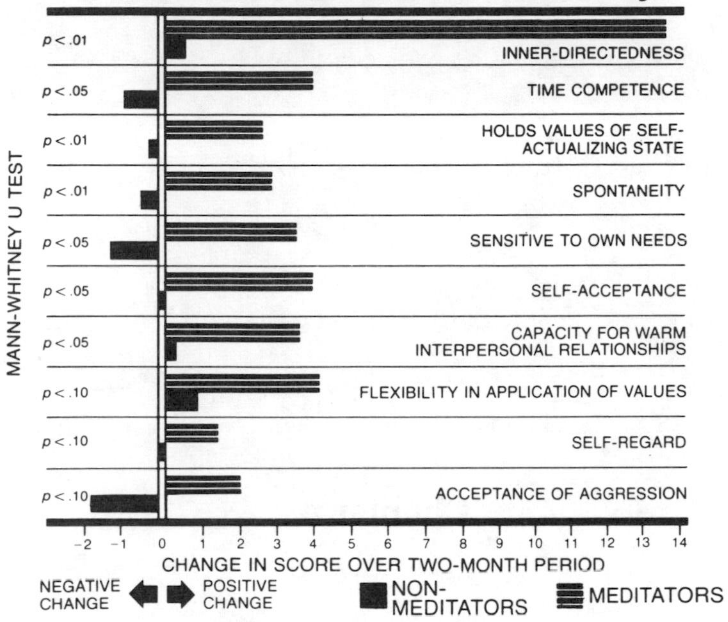

DEVELOPMENT OF PERSONALITY

Finding: Subjects practicing the Transcendental Meditation technique, measured once prior to beginning the technique and again two months later, showed significant positive improvement in the following traits when compared with a matched control group of non-meditators: inner-directedness, time competence, self-actualization, spontaneity, sensitivity to one's needs, self-acceptance, and capacity for warm interpersonal relationships. The test used was the Personal Orientation Inventory (POI). Two independent studies also using the POI confirmed these results.

Interpretation: The POI was developed by Shostrom to measure Maslow's concept of self-actualization. Maslow defines self-actualization as a high level of maturity, health, and fulfillment; transcendence of deficiencies; a clearer, more efficient perception of reality; more openness to experience; increased integration, wholeness, and unity of person; increased spontaneity, expressiveness, aliveness; a real self; increased objectivity, detachment, transcendence of self; ability to fuse concreteness and abstractness; ability to love; a firm identity, increased autonomy, and resistance to enculturation. All the personality changes brought about by the Transcendental Meditation program are clearly in the direction of what is generally recognized as the develpment of a healthy, self-actualized personality.

First Reference: Sanford Nidich, William Seeman, and Thomas Dreskin, "Influence of Transcendental Meditation: A Replication," *Journal of Counseling Psychology* 20, no. 6 (U.S.A.: 1973): 565-566.

Second Reference: William Seeman, Sanford Nidich, and Thomas Banta, "Influence of Transcendental Meditation on a Measure of Self-Actualization," *Journal of Counseling Psychology* 19, no. 3 (U.S.A.: 1972): 184-187.

Third Reference: Larry A. Hjelle, "Transcendental Meditation and Psychological Health," *Perceptual and Motor Skills* 39 (U.S.A: 1974): 623-628.

Chapter 4

Learning the TM technique

If I decide to do it, how do I go about learning the TM technique.

You can learn the Transcendental Meditation technique in seven steps. They are:

A. Introductory steps:
  1. *Introductory lecture.* If you've read our book thus far you are already acquainted with the introductory material (What can the TM program do for me?).
  2. *Preparatory lecture.* This lecture is about the practice of the TM technique—specific explanations of how the technique works, how it differs from other techniques, where it comes from, how it is taught, and why it is taught in that way.
  3. *Personal interview.* Just after the preparatory lecture, you meet with a teacher of the TM program, get to know each other, and clear up any questions you may have.

B. Four consecutive days of instruction (two hours each day):
  4. *Personal instruction.* This is the private session where you learn the TM technique from your teacher, who was personally trained and qualified by Maharishi Mahesh Yogi.
  5. *First day checking.* In this group session you receive further instruction and answers to your questions about your experiences while discussing practical details about the TM program.
  6. *Second day checking.* The group discusses the mechanics of the process of the TM technique and the release of stress in the light of their experience with the practice.
  7. *Third day checking.* This group session explores the goal of the TM program—life free from stress, with the full use of mental and physical potential.

Is that all?

About ten days after you begin, you'll come back for another meeting with your class and teacher to get the answers to any questions that may have occurred to you, and to be sure that the practice is going well. And you can come in any time, to any World Plan center (anywhere in the world—see page 223, 224), as often as you like. There, regular checking is available to make sure that the practice of the TM technique is correct. Also, centers have many optional lectures on the TM technique, the whole TM program, and the Science of Creative Intelligence.

Are there any requirements for starting the Transcendental Meditation program?

Yes.

I knew there was a catch!

Three catches. The first and most important is a commitment of time. You must be able to go to all the sessions—both of the first two lectures, the interview, and most important, all four consecutive sessions of instruction. And you should set aside 15–20 minutes, twice a day, for the regular practice of the TM technique.

What if I haven't learned how in four sessions?

You learn how in the *first* session! The next three are for confirming your understanding, and explaining how the technique works. It is *very* easy to learn, and the teaching procedures are specifically designed to ensure that everyone learns quickly and easily. If you'd like more instruction or have any questions about the TM technique you can come into the center for verification of the practice—we call it "checking." The entire TM program, including unlimited checking and many lecture programs, is included in the course fee.

Course fee?

As of 1975, the course fee in the USA is $125 per person. Couples, and their children under 15, may all start together for $200. The fee for college students is $65, for high school students $55, and for junior high school students $35. Children between four and ten are asked to bring two weeks' allowance.

What's the money used for?

All the organizations that teach the TM program are nonprofit, tax-exempt, educational organizations. There are costs involved in teaching the technique and in maintaining an organization so that anyone can learn—renting halls and rooms, printing pamphlets and posters, advertising, teachers' salaries—all basic expenses which each person meets when he begins the TM course.

As we mentioned, the one-time course fee includes the four sessions of instruction, and unlimited checking of the TM technique, plus the optional weekly meetings and other activities at each center.

For happiness, growing every day, it's ridiculously low, especially when compared to other programs you may have considered and other ways we spend money for enjoyment in life.

So that's two requirements—what's number three?

The third is that you refrain from any nonprescription "recreational" drugs for fifteen days prior to personal instruction. By nonprescription "recreational" drugs we mean marijuana, LSD, amphetamines, barbiturates, narcotics—anything your doctor did not prescribe.

Why no nonprescription drugs for fifteen days?

Drugs alter perception (that's the point of taking them in the first place). It's necessary for perception to be as natural as possible so that the TM technique can be learned most easily and effectively.

But the effects of these drugs seem to wear off in a few hours, or at most, a few days. Why wait fifteen days?

The very subtle effects of these drugs do persist long after the more obvious effects. Scientific research on these drugs shows that it takes at least fifteen days for the system to be reasonably clear of residual effects. Experience teaching the TM technique to hundreds of thousands of people has shown this clarity to be essential for the right start of the technique.

What about aspirin, or prescription drugs?

It's not necessary to stop taking aspirin and other "over the counter' medicines. Also, we don't interfere with the doctors' prescriptions—if a doctor prescribes some drug, it's important for maintaining health.

May I drink before I begin the TM technique?

Not within a few hours of beginning—and we suggest that you not drink more than your usual amount of alcohol for a day or two before you begin.

What about cigarettes?

Tobacco doesn't seem to interfere with the effective start of the TM technique.

Do I need to meet all these requirements just to come to the introductory lecture?

No—the introductory and preparatory lectures are to introduce the TM program, clear away misconceptions, and to give some basic information about the practice. You can come to these any time, even several times if you like. Of course, there is no charge for these talks. When you decide you'd like to start the technique, then the requirements become relevant.

How does the TM technique work?

The important thing about the TM technique is that it produces an experience—a concrete, specific, lively experience. The description of an experience is bound to be abstract. As we mentioned before, imagine describing the taste of a strawberry. But the experience of a strawberry is very real—as is the experience of the TM technique.

Already, we've said many times that the TM technique is effortless, spontaneous, and natural. Now to be more specific, the TM technique works on the basis of the natural tendency of the mind.

Natural tendency of the mind?

Yes, to enjoy more and more. As we have explained, the field of pure creative intelligence is the source of all energy and intelligence, so it is very attractive and the attention naturally goes there. All we need is a technique.

Thoughts come from this source, the field of pure creative intelligence. All thoughts, as we usually experience them, are directed outward, through thinking and speech, and then into action. During the TM technique, we take a specific thought, our "mantra." Because of the nature of the mantra, and the way we are taught to experience it, the mind automatically goes within, following the thought of the mantra back to the source of all thought. Each "step" toward pure consciousness is more and more fulfilling, and the final step—the experience of pure creative intelligence—is the most fulfilling of all.

Mantra?

"Mantra" means a specific sound, the effects of which are known for the individual in every way—mentally, physically, and environmentally. The ones used in the TM program come from an ancient tradition which assures their beneficial effectiveness. They are taught in a very specific way. Everyone learns individually and privately, from a teacher personally trained and qualified by Maharishi Mahesh Yogi. The teaching procedure is a very simple exchange of information and instructions between the teacher and the student. The teacher gives some instruction and the student follows it. Then, the teacher asks some question and, on the basis of the answer, gives some further instruction. The student is lead *innocently*—that's the key word—to the experience of transcending, the experience of pure creative intelligence.

What does the TM experience feel like?

Different people describe the experience in different ways—very quiet, deeply peaceful, calm, so easy to do, etc. But is important to remember that we practice the technique for its results in activity, not for any particular experience *during* the practice.

If it is so easy, why don't you just print a list of mantras and a few directions and I can learn from a book?

There are several reasons. First, there's that interchange between teacher and student which ensures that you have correct experiences. Second, it's necessary that the mantra be personally selected by a trained teacher, and that it be imparted properly and usefully.

So you need the correct mantra, properly selected, properly given, and properly used. These three elements are essentials for effortless, effective practice of the Transcendental Meditation technique.

Where do the mantras come from?

They come from a very old tradition of great teachers that goes back thousands of years. The nearest teacher to us in this tradition is Maharishi's teacher, Guru Dev, His Divinity Swami Brahmananda Saraswati, who had the wisdom and insight to revive this great teaching.

Where does Maharishi come in?

Maharishi has been teaching continuously throughout the world since 1959. This has been in response to the tremendous need of our age for a simple technique to accomplish so much. Everywhere he goes, he inspires people with his vision of a world free from suffering. He personally trains and qualifies all teachers of the TM program and, through his inspiration he guides all phases of the movement.

What is the movement?

The TM program is taught through five organizations coordinated by the World Plan Executive Council:

Students International Meditation Society—for students and youth

International Meditation Society—for the general adult community

Spiritual Regeneràtion Movement—for those interested in a spiritual approach to life, and for retired people.

Foundation for the Science of Creative Intelligence—for business, management, industry, and the professional community

Maharishi International University—a university to relate the study of creative intelligence to all disciplines of knowledge.

These five organizations together compose the World Plan center in each area.

Where do I go to learn the TM technique?

Write or call the nearest center in the list at the back of the book. They'll tell you the address of your local World Plan center.

And if I have more questions?

The teachers at your local World Plan center will be delighted to answer them.

Chapter 5

the TM Program: Solution to All Problems?

All problems! You folks are mighty ambitious!

Consider how mankind has gone about solving problems so far. We examine the problem, think about it, do something. Perhaps what we do is effective, perhaps not. Perhaps in a little while it is obvious that the side effects of our "solution" are worse than the problem. Clearly, our world situation indicates that more creativity and intelligence are essential.

Consider the problem of darkness. Suppose a room is full of darkness, and those in the room want to eliminate the darkness. They might form a committee—THE COMMITTEE ON DARKNESS.

THIS COMMITTEE ON DARKNESS WILL NOW COME TO ORDER.

THE SECRETARY WILL NOW READ THE MINUTES OF THE LAST MEETING.

I CAN'T READ THESE– IT'S TOO DARK IN HERE.

ANY OLD BUSINESS?

YEAH! IT'S DARK IN HERE– LET'S GET RID OF THIS DARKNESS.

ANY REPORTS?

WE TRIED PUTTING THE DARKNESS IN A BOX AND THROWING IT OUT...

DID IT WORK?

IT'S STILL DARK, ISN'T IT?

WE LOOKED FOR THE HOLE WHERE DARKNESS WAS COMING IN... COULDN'T FIND IT.

I THINK THAT RATHER THAN GET RID OF THIS DARKNESS WE SHOULD ACCEPT IT AS A NATURAL PART OF LIFE. WE SHOULD BE PROUD OF IT— **IT'S OUR BIRTHRIGHT!**

LET'S START A PUBLICITY CAMPAIGN TO REVISE THE PUBLIC IMAGE OF DARKNESS.

HERE! HERE!

A SLOGAN! WE NEED A SLOGAN!

"GIMME A 7, GIMME A 6, GIMME A 5,4,3! DARKNESS, DARKNESS, THAT'S FOR ME!"

A SONG! WE NEED A SONG! HOW ABOUT, "DANCING IN THE DARK"!?

QUIET— I HEAR FOOTSTEPS.

CLUMP
CLUMP
CLUMP
CLICK!

?
?
?
?
?
?
?
?

What the committee tried to do was solve the problem of darkness on the level of the problem.

This "problem" of darkness is simply the absence of light. We turn on the light and the problem of darkness is gone. This is the principle of introducing the "second element," which in this case is light.

Fine, but what does this have to do with the TM program?

The TM technique infuses strength, stability, creativity, and intelligence into human life. A problem is simply the inability to deal with some situation—when ability is increased, the "problem" becomes an easy task, a challenge, or even a pleasure. The TM program eliminates the root of all problems—weakness.

Interesting principle, but it still seems very impractical.

Alright, let's explore it a little further. We'll consider some of our current problems and explain how the TM program solves them.

What about the problem of education? Many students find it boring and a waste of time.

There are two important aspects of education: factual knowledge and individual ability. Most education today offers only one of these aspects the study of *facts* about this and that. But the more we study any field, the more we realize how much we do not know and the more we question the practical value of what we're learning. What's missing is the personal aspect, the development of the student's own *ability* to learn. The TM program provides this second aspect to education. It develops the capacity to know, expanding the "container" of knowledge.

When a student is practicing the TM program, every day his mind is fresher and more alert. Perception is keener and the intellect is sharper. The ability to integrate grows so that all knowledge can be constructively and holistically applied in such away that the student finds education enjoyable, relevant, and rewarding.

What about a job that involves a tremendous amount of routine. There doesn't seem to be much chance to display creative intelligence there.

Routine work is necessary for progress, yet we've all experienced the boredom and frustration that it brings. Whenever growth is obstructed, whenever creative intelligence does not find an opportunity for full expression in life, then we begin to feel uncomfortable. This discomfort is the seat of frustration, and this frustration is the basis of all problems in life.

What is needed is some way for awareness to grow, for creativity and intelligence to express themselves. The TM program does just this. During the TM technique, the mind goes beyond the boundaries of routine to the unbounded field of creative intelligence. This sense of widened perception removes the frustration and brings freshness and enjoyment into life, even into routine, it is this sense that enables us to perceive more and more avenues of expression for our growing creativity—at work, at home, with our friends, and in the community.

What about mental health? I hear that one half of the hospital beds in the United States are taken by mental patients.

First, regular practice of the TM technique is excellent insurance against mental illness, as we've already discussed.

Further, the TM program shows remarkable potential in therapy of mental patients. It is very easy to do, easy to teach, and inexpensive. And it works! Many patients who haven't responded to any therapy show improvement with the TM technique.

What about society's problems—poverty, unemployment, and all those?

The TM program increases creativity and intelligence. With those two qualities we can solve all these other problems. More lively and creative people find that they're no longer in poverty, no longer unemployed. The nature of life—which is to progress and expand—takes over, and life becomes not a struggle, but a joy.

What's needed is to integrate creative thinking with constructive activity for the good of all.

How about crime?

Crime is based on weakness. If someone has desires that he cannot fulfill lawfully, he is tempted to commit crimes. The TM program strengthens the mind while improving creativity and intelligence. It removes this basic weakness. The TM program has been successfully used to rehabilitate prisoners.

Rehabilitation of Prisoners I

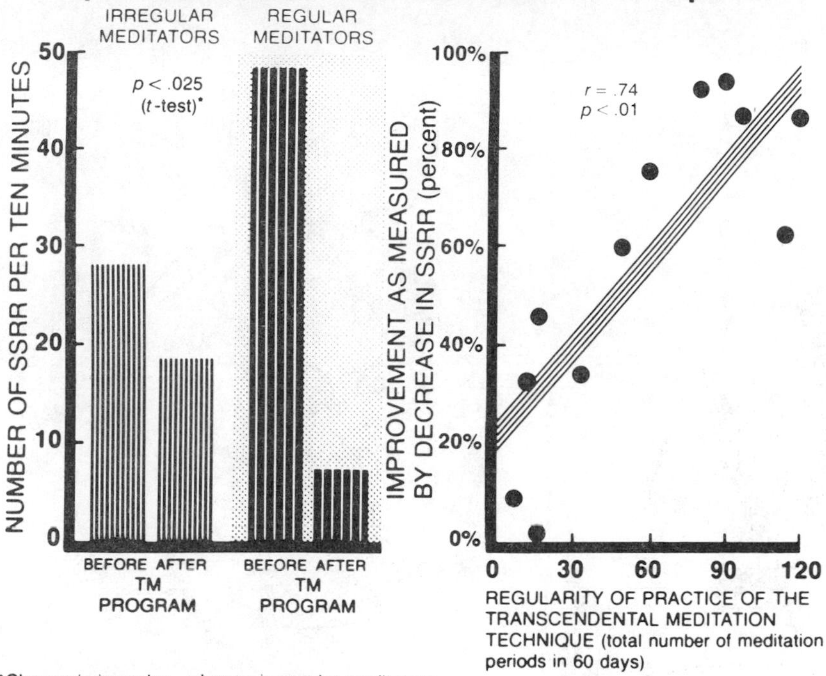

REHABILITATION OF PRISONERS I: IMPROVED PHYSIOLOGY

Finding: The Transcendental Meditation technique reduced the level of stress in prisoners, as measured physiologically by number of spontaneous skin resistance responses (SSRR). The study showed that regular practice of the TM technique was positively correlated with the degree of increase in autonomic stability.

Interpretation: The Transcendental Meditation program is a truly effective means for rehabilitation, because it stabilizes the prisoner's physiology allowing him to direct his energies more positively and to assume more responsibility for his life.

Reference: David W. Orme-Johnson, John Kiehlbauch, Richard Moore, and John Bristol, "Personality and Autonomic Changes in Prisoners Practicing the Transcendental Meditation Technique," (La Tuna Federal Penitentiary, New Mexico, U.S.A.).

Rehabilitation of Prisoners II

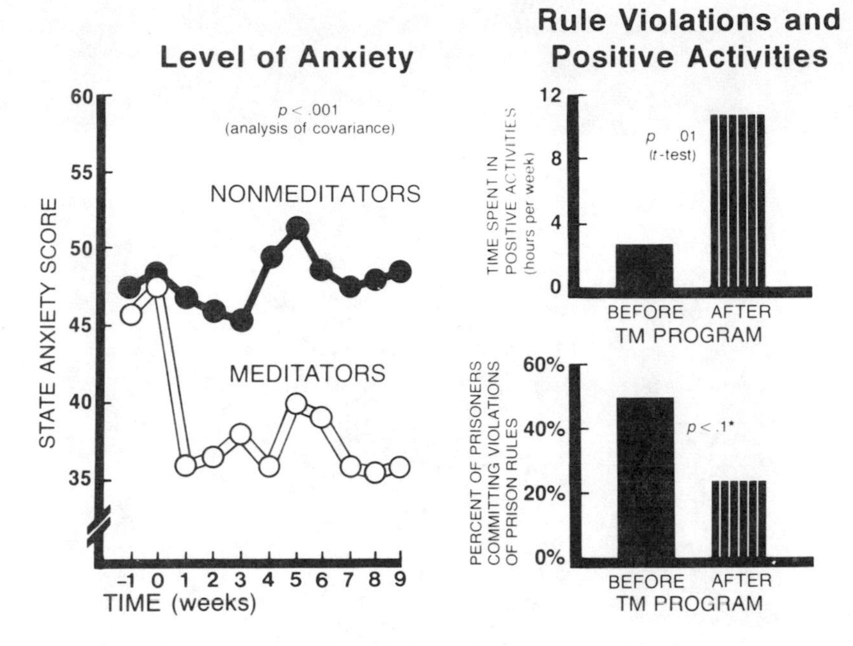

* Mann-Whitney U test comparing meditators and nonmeditators.

REHABILITATION OF PRISONERS II: IMPROVED SOCIAL BEHAVIOR

Finding: Three measures on prisoners practicing the Transcendental Meditation technique indicated:

1. a reduction in anxiety, as measured by the Spielberger State-Trait Anxiety Inventory (STAI)
2. a reduction in prison rule violations
3. an increase in time spent in positive activities

Interpretation: The Transcendental Meditation program produces the physiological and psychological normalization necessary for true and lasting rehabilitation.

First Reference: David Ballou, "The Transcendental Meditation Program at Stillwater Prison," (University of Kansas, Lawrence, Kansas, U.S.A.).

Second Reference: Monte Cunningham and Walter Koch, "The Transcendental Meditation Program and Rehabilitation: A Pilot Project at the Federal Correctional Institution at Lompoc, California."

It breaks the cycle of crime—prison—more crime. . .

Couldn't a person become a more creative criminal?

No. The strength to act correctly, in harmony with nature and society, and the clear perception of the practicality of right action grow as creativity grows.

Drug abuse?

Reduced Drug Abuse

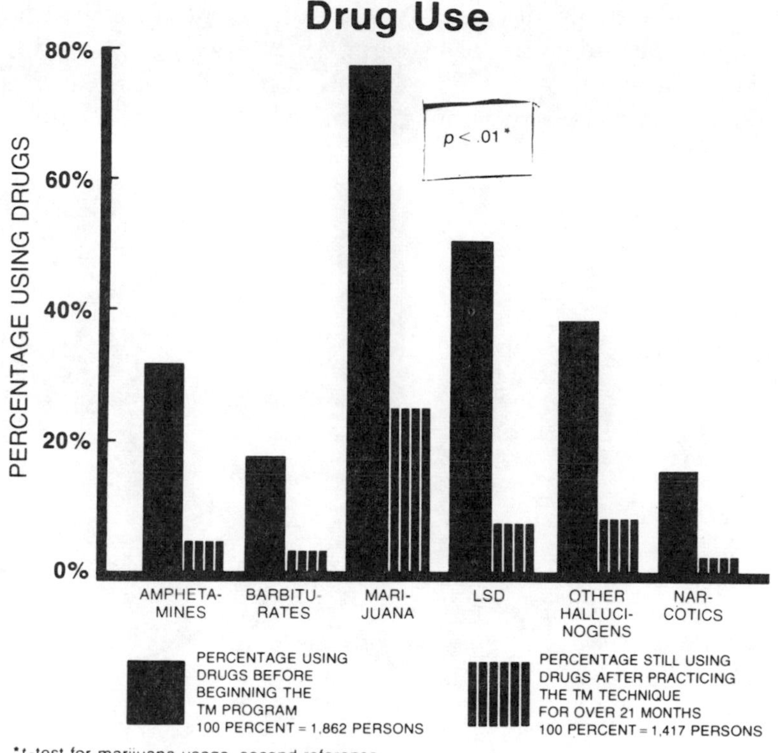

REDUCED DRUG ABUSE (USA)

Finding: A retrospective study of 1,862 subjects who practiced the Transcendental Meditation technique an average of 20 months showed decreases in the reported use of non-prescribed drugs.

Among the 852 subjects who had practiced the TM technique over 22 months, only 12.2% used marijuana, 3% used LSD, 4% used other hallucinogens, 1.2% used narcotics, 1.2% used amphetamines, and 1% used barbiturates. Nearly all these subjects who continued to use drugs reported using them only very rarely.

Interpretation: Because the Transcendental Meditation program improves inner control and decreases anxiety and strengthens mental health and general well-being, it may be concluded that the desire for drugs is thereby decreased or eliminated. This study indicates that the Transcendental Meditation program may be the most effective antidote for drug abuse, because its success does not depend on any initial resolve on the part of the subject to discontinue bad habits.

First Reference: Herbert Benson and Robert Keith Wallace, "Decreased Drug Abuse with Transcendental Meditation: A Study of 1,862 Subjects," *Drug Abuse: Proceedings of the International Conference*, ed., Chris J. D. Zarafonetis (Philadelphia, Pennsylvania, U.S.A.: Lea and Febiger, 1972): 369–376 and *Congressional Record*, Serial No. 92–1 (Washington, D.C., U.S.A.: Government Printing Office, 1971).

People seem to take drugs for one of two reasons: either for fulfillment, which the TM program provides, or for escape, which the program eliminates the need for. The TM technique is deeply satisfying. The increased success in activity is also satisfying. Drug abuse seems to drop away because the desire for the drugs is gone.

A Prisoner at
Niedershönenfeld Prison
Germany

"For three years I was totally dependent on morphine. Then after breaking into a chemist's shop and being sent to prison I was forced to give up hard drugs.

"This did not mean that I no longer desired drugs; there was hardly a day when I did not think of the syringe, it just depended on my mood— sometimes more, sometimes less.

"The urge to use the syringe behind bars was much greater because I thought it would make me totally free.

"This is what I thought until I started the Transcendental Meditation program. I very soon discovered that my thoughts turned less towards drugs and today I don't even think about drugs at all. I am very happy about that. I know that man's desire for freedom can only be satisfied by meditation because meditation means to be free.

"I look forward to many more such insights."

G. LeDain, et al.
Report of the Commission of Inquiry
into the Non-Medicinal Use of Drugs
21 January 1972
Canada

"Most of the respondents (61.1 percent) believed that the Transcendental Meditation program was extremely important in reducing or ending their drug use."

Paul Andrews
Project Director
Drug Education
Commonwealth of Massachusetts

"The TM program is without question a non-chemical alternative to drug abuse."

Melba Shepard
Executive Director
Boulder Youth Services

"We have had some experience with the Transcendental Meditation process and have found that it can be a factor in reduction of drug abuse."

What about alcohol and cigarettes?

Reduced Use of Alcohol and Cigarettes

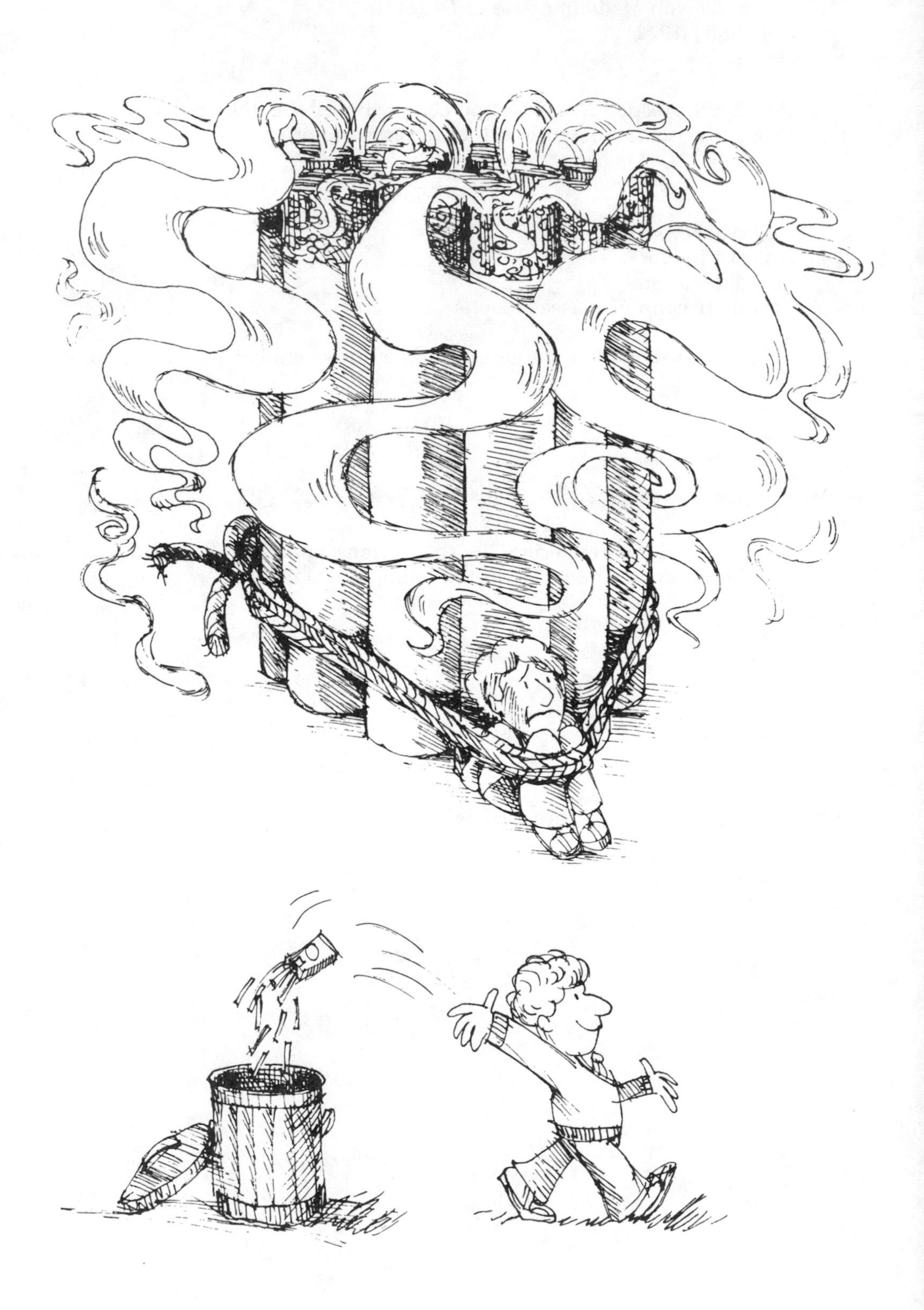

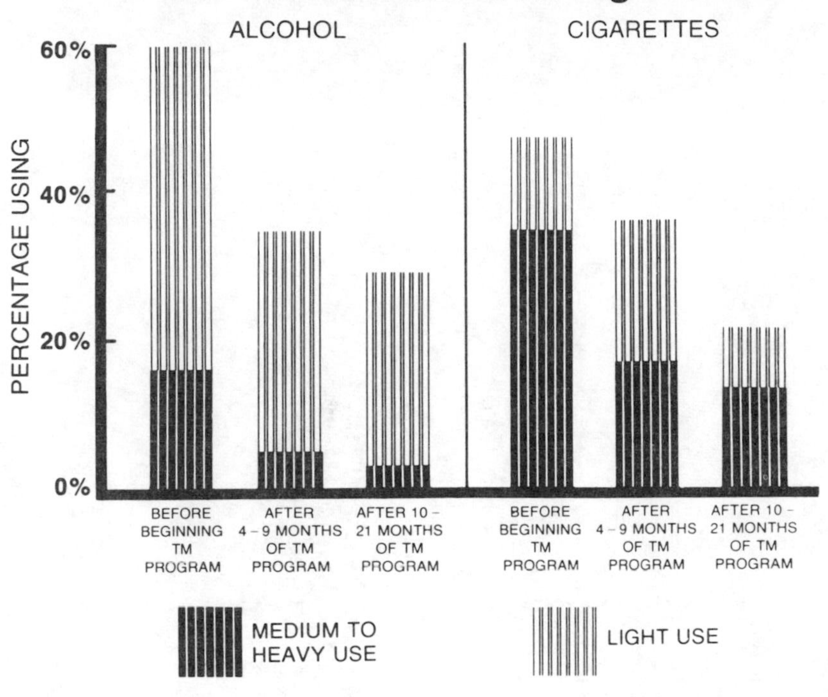

REDUCED USE OF ALCOHOL AND CIGARETTES

Finding: A retrospective study of 1,862 subjects who had practiced the Transcendental Meditation technique an average of 20 months showed a significant reduction in the reported use of alcohol and cigarettes.

Interpretation: The Transcendental Meditation technique has been shown to provide deep relaxation to the entire nervous system and to remove tensions, giving rise to a more calm, restful, and creative functioning of mind and body. These effects may be taken to explain the gradual decrease in the need for alcohol and cigarettes seen in this study.

Reference: Herbert Benson and Robert Keith Wallace, "Decreased Drug Abuse with Transcendental Meditation: A Study of 1,862 Subjects," *Drug Abuse: Proceedings of the International Conference*, ed. Chris J. D. Zarafonetis (Philadelphia, Pennsylvania, U.S.A.: Lea and Febiger, 1972): 369–376 and *Congressional Record*, Serial No. 92–1 (Washington, D.C., U.S.A.: Government Printing Office, 1971).

What about prejudice and bad feeling among groups of people?

There will always be different groups of people, different cultures, and different ways of life.

Problems arise when a narrow awareness and stress produce rigid boundaries among groups. The TM program develops appreciation and the ability to harmonize differences. Then these differences co-exist and can be appreciated for their own value.

STRESS

HARMONY

Increased Tolerance in High School Students

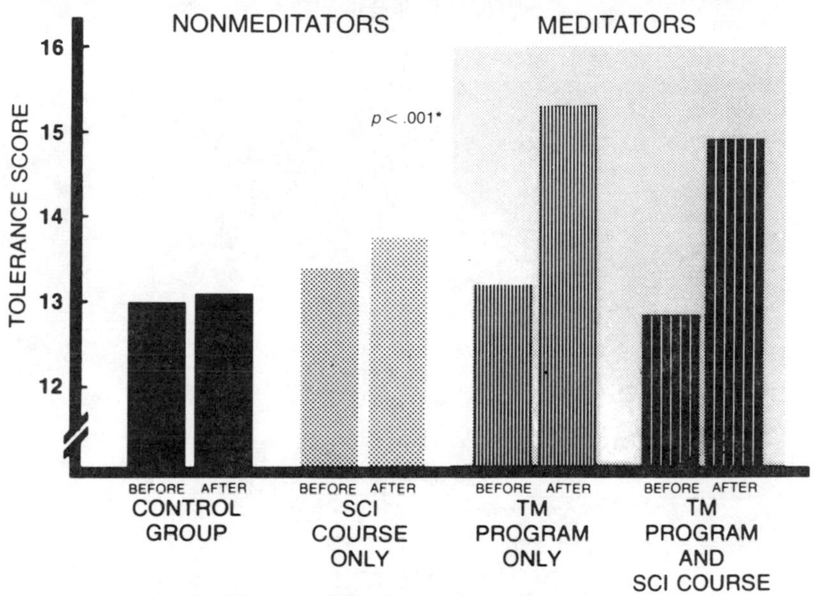

INCREASED TOLERANCE IN HIGH SCHOOL STUDENTS

Finding: In a study of 80 students at a public high school in Canada, students who practiced the Transcendental Meditation technique showed a significant increase in tolerance ($p<.001$) after 14 weeks of the TM program, as measured by the Jackson Personality Inventory, whereas the control group did not. The increase in tolerance was shown to be primarily due to the effects of the practice of the TM technique itself, and not simply to intellectual involvement with the theory underlying it, as presented in an accompanying Science of Creative Intelligence course.

Interpretation: This finding has extremely important implications for the modern urban high school, which is attended by students from many different ethnic and social backgrounds. Increased tolerance may be seen as the natural result of the greater self-confidence, warmth, and positivity shown to be developed by the TM program. On a deeper level, increased tolerance reflects an expanded area of identification coming from deeper experience of the self. The Transcendental Meditation program promises secondary education a means to develop this quality in its students as part of the regular curriculum.

Reference: Howard Shecter, "The Transcendental Meditation Program in the Classroom: A Psychological Evaluation," (York University, North York, Ontario, Canada).

Aren't cultures being absorbed into one another?

At the moment, to a great extent, yes. It is essential that the individuals in each culture have greater stability so that they can hold on to the values of their culture while taking full advantage of the tremendous progress of our age. With the TM technique, each person develops his own nature, and this includes his own cultural nature, in a stable, integrated way. From this firm platform we can review the achievements of other cultures, and the demands of technology and changing times, and accept only those ideas which really support and help our growth.

The only way different cultures will be preserved is if those in each culture practice the TM program so that we can remain stable in the values of our culture and not be at the mercy of the winds of change.

What about the environment—ecology?

The thousands of individual problems that make up the basic problem of ecological balance all require more creativity and intelligence for their solution.

Equally important, these problems must be solved in such a way that they do not create worse problems. They must be solved with a breadth of awareness that takes in the entire situation, by minds that intuitively select the course of action that is completely life-supporting.

The TM program develops his breadth of awareness and this spontaneous knowledge of right action.

Johannes Olivegren
Professor of Architecture
Chalmers University of Technology
Sweden

"In many parts of the world much of the modern man-made environment is destroying the natural beauty of our landscapes, making urban life hectic and dangerous and our homes and working places impersonal and uninspiring. The TM program will open the eyes and inspire the creativity of planners, architects, builders, politicians, and laymen so that our houses, cities and landscapes will be a more life-supporting environmental frame for a rich and harmonious life for everybody."

Simon Cohen
Senior Probation Officer
Hampshire Probation Service
Hampshire, England

"As the TM program frees people to use more of their full potential, it deepens their awareness of other people and the world they live in. When people change in this way their social and political systems must follow."

And world peace?

World peace is a problem of individual peace. For a forest to be green all the trees must be green. For us to have world peace we must start with each individual becoming fulfilled. This is the only possible basis for lasting world peace. And it is a *real* basis.

Governmental and community leaders around the globe have praised and endorsed the promise of the Transcendental Meditation program to establish a stable, better world. An appeal to the governments of the world, made by Members of Parliament from all the States of India, puts it very beautifully:

> "Live in peace or perish is the challenge of the nuclear age. The state of increasing tension cannot continue indefinitely; it must give way to peace or annihilation . . . Maharishi's simple Transcendental Meditation program bridges the gulf between the inner and outer aspects of life. It regenerates the personality improving all phases of life, resulting in a harmonious development of body, mind, and soul. . . . It is our national duty to alleviate atmospheric tensions as soon as possible by eliminating the tensions in the lives of every individual. This can best be accomplished by giving the people a simple technique of creating powerful influences of peace and harmony from the deepest level of their consciousness—by a few minutes of daily practice of the Transcendental Meditation technique. . . . Increased consciousness means greater energy, creative intelligence, better health and also greater harmony in social relationships. Maharishi's simple Transcendental Meditation technique is a direct way to it. It is only necessary for us all to adopt it."
>
> Taken from the text of an appeal made by Members of Parliament from all the States of India, 1963.

That sounds pretty far-reaching. But how do you get everyone in the world to participate in the TM program?

We don't need to. All we need is one person in one hundred, and the whole of society will enjoy the benefits.

One in one hundred? How can so few make any difference?

It was once thought that any program to improve the quality of life of society as a whole would have to directly involve a majority of the population. For several years, researchers have been studying the wide range of benefits that the Transcendental Meditation program produces in every area of individual life: health, psychology, efficiency, and creativity. Recently, sociological studies of more than one hundred cities in the U.S.A. revealed a striking and important new phenomenon taking place.

Sociologists found that when only 1% of a population is practicing the Transcendental Meditation program, the whole population suddenly begins to measurably increase its efficiency, orderliness, and productivity. This is phase transition——

Phase transition?

"Phase transition" is a term from physics and chemistry. It refers to a basic change in the orderliness of any natural system. The change from a drop of water to a snowflake is one example of phase transition. The crystalline structure of the snowflake is far more orderly than the random arrangement of molecules when water is in the liquid state.

Scientists doing research on the TM technique have speculated that a somewhat similar phase transition takes place producing a more orderly functioning of the neurons of the brain. In the same way, the phase transition model may apply to basic changes in society. We can think of the overall effect of the TM program as bringing a change in society, from a chaotic state to a more harmonious one.

Best of all, research has shown that an improvement in the quality of life does not necessarily require everyone to practice the TM technique.

Because of the concentrated influence of orderliness and balance that the TM program produces, 1% of the population practicing the program is enough to maintain the coherent functioning of the entire society.

This phase transition that begins when 1% is meditating was predicted on the basis of the natural laws in physics and other sciences and has now been borne out by a comprehensive survey of scores of cities in which 1% are practicing the TM program. For example, in matched *non* meditating cities the crime rate increased 7.7% in one year, but in cities reaching the 1% transition point the crime rate fell an average of 8.8%—a net improvement of nearly 17%.

Change in Crime Rate 1972–1973: Cities with One Percent of the Population Practicing the TM Technique Compared to Control Cities

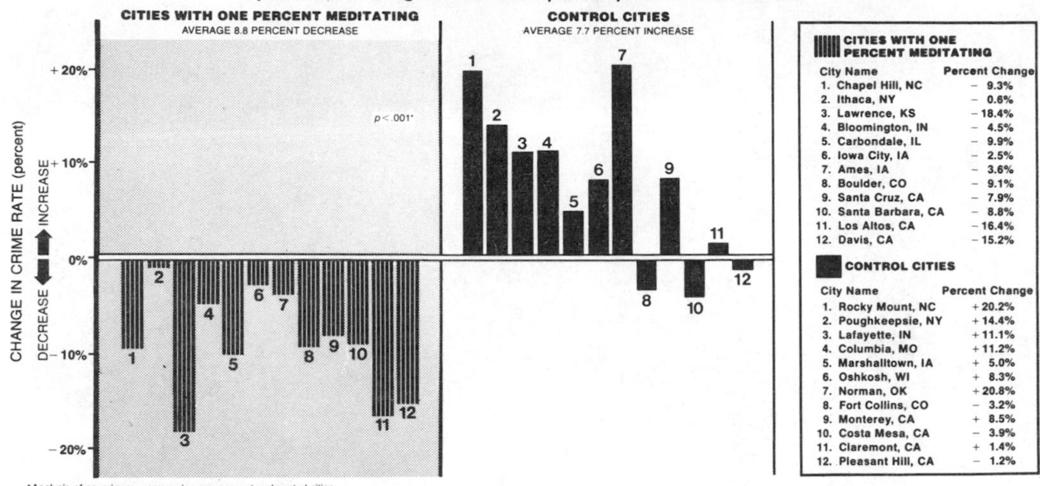

CITIES WITH ONE PERCENT MEDITATING

City Name	Percent Change
1. Chapel Hill, NC	− 9.3%
2. Ithaca, NY	− 0.6%
3. Lawrence, KS	−18.4%
4. Bloomington, IN	− 4.5%
5. Carbondale, IL	− 9.9%
6. Iowa City, IA	− 2.5%
7. Ames, IA	− 3.6%
8. Boulder, CO	− 9.1%
9. Santa Cruz, CA	− 7.9%
10. Santa Barbara, CA	− 8.8%
11. Los Altos, CA	−16.4%
12. Davis, CA	−15.2%

CONTROL CITIES

City Name	Percent Change
1. Rocky Mount, NC	+20.2%
2. Poughkeepsie, NY	+14.4%
3. Lafayette, IN	+11.1%
4. Columbia, MO	+11.2%
5. Marshalltown, IA	+ 5.0%
6. Oshkosh, WI	+ 8.3%
7. Norman, OK	+20.8%
8. Fort Collins, CO	− 3.2%
9. Monterey, CA	+ 8.5%
10. Costa Mesa, CA	− 3.9%
11. Claremont, CA	+ 1.4%
12. Pleasant Hill, CA	− 1.2%

*Analysis of covariance—comparing one percent and control cities.

DECREASED CRIME IN THE ENVIRONMENT OF INCREASING CRIME IMPROVED QUALITY OF CITY LIFE

Finding: This retrospective study compared 12 cities in which at least one percent of the population had learned the Transcendental Meditation technique by the end of 1972 to 12 matched control cities with relatively few people practicing the TM technique but otherwise comparable in population, location, and crime statistics. Nine of the 12 control cities increased in number of serious crimes from 1972 to 1973 with an average change of +7.7 percent. According to the FBI Uniform Crime Reports for the nation as a whole, the average increase in crime that year in cities of comparable size was 8.7 percent. In contrast, the cities with one percent of their population practicing the TM technique decreased in crime rate by an average of 8.8 percent, a relative decrease of 16.5 percent when compared with the control group.

This difference in change in crime rate between the two groups of cities was statistically significant ($p < .001$, analysis of co-variance). Furthermore, the correlation between percentage of meditators and decrease in crime rate for cities in this sample was 0.66 ($p < .001$), a statistically significant degree of correlation.

Interpretation: Any sociological study has many uncontrolled variables, making it difficult to prove definitely a relationship of cause and effect. In this case, however, the effect seen is consistent over many cities. Furthermore, the many dramatically proven effects of improved orderliness of physiology and psychology and improved interpersonal relationships seen in individuals practicing the Transcendental Meditation technique suggest that a group of individuals practicing the technique cannot help but influence the quality of life of the whole population. Increased harmony and balance in an individual's behavior naturally increase harmony and balance in the life of the city. This initial survey indicates that one percent of a city's population practicing the TM technique is sufficient to bring about a noticeable transformation in the quality of life.

Reference: Candace Borland and Garland Landrith III, "Influence of the Transcendental Meditation Program on Crime Rate in Cities," (Maharishi International University, Fairfield, Iowa, U.S.A.).

The fact that the crime rate drops so significantly in most 1% TM cities shows that the positive influence of the people practicing the Transcendental Meditation program reaches all the way through the fabric of society. Think how much *more* effect this increased orderliness must have on people who are already involved in constructive and useful behavior for the good of society!

Hundreds of research programs around the world have verified the beneficial effects of the Transcendental Meditation program in individual life. Now an important breakthrough in the field of sociology has revealed the capability of the program to enable us to solve the age-old problems of mankind in this generation.

This research establishes that a person practicing the TM technique has so profound an influence on his surroundings that any community, city, state, or nation can easily reach phase transition in a few weeks or months. And after the transition point is achieved, increasing progress and improvement of society are both spontaneous and inevitable.

This graph of nations approaching phase transition shows that the dawning of The Age of Enlightenment, (that is, an age when everyone uses his full potential) is not only a scientific possibility—it has already begun. Any country can be the first to set a global example of peace and prosperity for the whole human race.

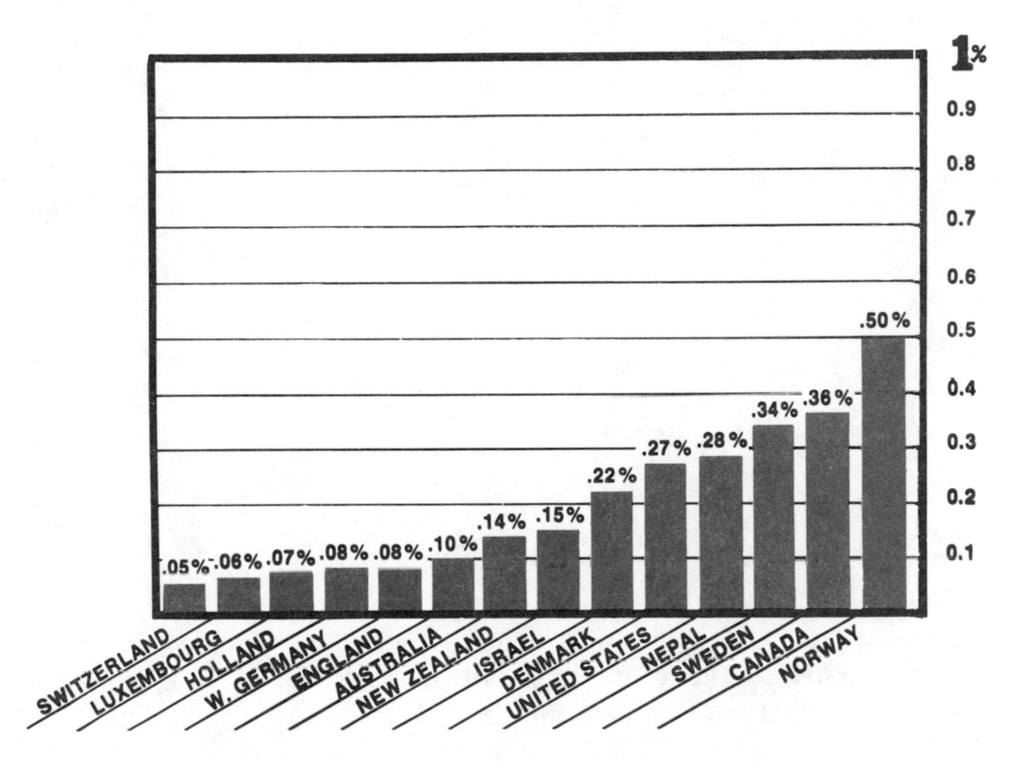

This is why there is a World Plan, to make the TM technique available everywhere by establishing a center for teaching the technique and training teachers among each million people. This plan is dedicated to accomplishing seven goals:

1. To develop the full potential of the individual
2. To improve governmental achievements
3. To realize the highest ideal of education
4. To eliminate the age-old problem of crime and all behavior that brings unhappiness to the family of man
5. To maximize the intelligent use of the environment
6. To bring fulfillment to the economic aspirations of individuals and society
7. To achieve the spiritual goals of mankind in this generation

So you see, the TM program presents a very holistic approach to the solution of problems because it is an intimate experience that touches the heart of all of us, and thus moves to change the face of the world from suffering to progress. We live in a very great, fortunate time.

I'll take it!

MAJOR WORLD PLAN CENTERS IN USA

There are over 380 neighborhood centers in the U.S. For the one nearest you, ask the telephone information operator for "Transcendental Meditation" or contact the national center 1015 Gayley Ave., LA., CA 90024

Atlanta
3615 N. Stratford Rd. N.E.
Atlanta, Georgia 30342
phone: 404 262-2902

Berkeley
2716 Derby Street
Berkeley, Calif. 94705
phone: 415 548-1144

Boston
73 Newbury Street
Boston, Mass. 02116
phone: 617 226-3770

Cambridge
33 Garden Street
Cambridge, Mass. 02138
phone: 617 876-4581

Charlotte
1724 East Seventh Street
Charlotte, N.C. 28204
phone: 704 332-6694

Chicago
604 Davis Street
Evanston, Ill. 60201
phone: 312 864-1810

Cincinnati
3960 Winding Way
Cincinnati, Ohio 45229
phone: 513 281-5296

Columbus
1818 W. Lane Ave.
Columbus, Ohio 43221
phone: 614 486-9298

Denver
240 St. Paul
Suite 102
Denver, Colorado 80206
phone: 303 320-4007

Des Moines
1311 34th Street
Des Moines, Iowa 50311
phone: 515 255-1547

Detroit
Colonial Federal Building
Suite 204
63 Kercheval
Grosse Pointe, Mich. 48236
phone: 313 882-7211

Hartford
5 Lincoln Street
Hartford, Conn. 06106
phone: 203 247-6733

Honolulu
227 S. King Street
Honolulu, Hawaii 96813
phone: 808 533-2335

Houston
2518 Drexel
Houston, Texas 77027
phone: 713 627-7500

Kansas City
6301 Main Street
Kansas City, Mo. 64113
phone: 816 523-5777

Los Angeles
1015 Gayley Ave.
Los Angeles, Calif. 90024
phone: 213 478-1569

Miami
2929 S.W. 3rd Ave.
4th Floor Suite
Miami, Florida 33129
phone: 305 854-7850

Milwaukee
400 E. Silver Spring
Whitefish Bay, Wisc. 53217
phone: 414 962-2300

Minneapolis
720 Washington Ave, S.E.
Suite 200
Minneapolis, Minn. 55414
phone: 612 331-9135

New Haven
1974 Yale Station
New Haven, Conn. 06520
phone: 203 776-5784

New York
Wentworth Building
59 W. 46th Street
New York, N.Y. 10036
phone: 212 586-3331

Philadelphia
1712 Locust Street
Philadelphia, Penn. 19103
phone: 215 732-9220

Pittsburgh
5871 Forbes Ave.
Pittsburgh, Penn. 15217
phone: 412 521-6000

Portland
7743 S.W. Capitol Highway
Portland, Oregon 97219
phone: 503 244-9377

Sacramento
2015 J Street, Suite 32
Sacramento, Calif. 95814
phone: 916 443-4895

St. Louis
742 Emerson Road
St. Louis, Mo. 63141
phone: 314 569-0020

San Francisco
218 11th Ave.
San Francisco, Calif. 94118
phone: 415 387-0223

Seattle
P.O. Box 21051
Seattle, Wash. 98111
phone: 206 322-1800

Washington, D.C.
2127 Leroy Place N.W.
Washington, D.C. 20008
phone: 202 387-5050

MAJOR WORLD PLAN CENTERS IN CANADA

There are over 80 neighborhood centers in Canada. For the one nearest you, call or write the one on this list that is closest to you.

Calgary
218-11th Avenue, S.W.
Calgary
Alberta T2R 0C3
phone: 403 245-1851

Edmonton
9320-83rd Avenue
Edmonton
Alberta T6C 1B8
phone: 403 365-6620

Halifax
6212 Allan Street, Apt. 6
Halifax
N.S. B3L 1G6
phone: 902 422-5905

Hamilton
271 Aberdeen Avenue
Hamilton
Ontario L8P 2R4
phone: 416 529-0190

Moncton
256 Cameron Street
Moncton
N.B. E1C 5Z3
phone: 506 855-0225

Montreal West
3666 Lorne Crescent
Montreal
P.Q. H2X 2B3
phone: 514 285-1298

Ottawa
65 Bank St-2
Ottawa
Ontario KIP 5N2
phone: 613 236-0000

Quebec
1085 Avenue des Erables
Quebec
P.Q. G1R 2N3
phone: 418 529-2149

Regina
2919 Angus Street
Regina
Saskatchewan S4S 1P1
phone: 306 586-4012

Saskatoon
707 University Drive
Saskatoon
Saskatchewan S7W 0J3
phone: 306 242-6317

Sudbury
262 Edmond St.
Sudbury
Ontario P3E 1M2
phone: 705 675-8405

Toronto
1483A Yonge Street
Toronto
Ontario M4T 1Z2
phone: 416 923-2264

Vancouver
1170 Hornby St., #202
Vancouver
B.C. V6Z 1V8
phone: 604 688-1728

Victoria
1270 Pandora Avenue
Victoria
B.C. V8V 3R4
phone: 604 383-9822

Winnepeg
51 Horace Street
Winnipeg
Manitoba R2H 0V8
phone: 204 247-5565

INTERNATIONAL WORLD PLAN CENTERS

The TM program is taught in over 90 countries throughout the world. For the address of the center nearest you write to either of the centers below:

World Plan Executive Council
Seelisberg
Switzerland

Academy of Meditation
Shankaracharya Nagar
Rishikesh
U.P.
India